ADVANCED MODULAR M

Statistics
3 & 4

for A and AS level
The University of London modular mathematics syllabus

Stephen Webb and Gerald Westover
for

NATIONAL
EXTENSION
COLLEGE

CollinsEducational
An Imprint of HarperCollins*Publishers*

Published by Collins Educational
An imprint of HarperCollins*Publishers*
77–85 Fulham Palace Road
Hammersmith
London W6 8JB
© National Extension College Trust Ltd 1997
First published 1997
ISBN 0 00322416 3

This book was written by Stephen Webb and Gerald Westover for the National Extension College Trust Ltd.

Designed by Derek Lee

Cover design and implementation by Derek Lee
Page layout by Mary Bishop
Project editor Anne Rooney

The authors and publishers thank Clive Morris and Graham Smithers for their comments on this book.

Printed and bound in the UK by Scotprint Ltd, Musselburgh

The National Extension College is an educational trust and a registered charity with a distinguished body of trustees. It is an independent, self-financing organisation.

Since it was established in 1963, NEC has pioneered the development of flexible learning for adults. NEC is actively developing innovative materials and systems for distance-learning options from basic skills and general education to degree and professional training.

For further details of NEC resources that support Advanced Modular Mathematics, and other NEC courses, contact NEC Customer Services:

National Extension College Trust Ltd
18 Brooklands Avenue
Cambridge CB2 2HN
Telephone 01223 316644, Fax 01223 313586

CONTENTS

Permissions

We are grateful to the following examination boards for permission to reproduce questions from past examination papers in the text and in the Exercises at the end of each section:

Associated Examining Board

EdExcel Foundation

University of Cambridge Local Examinations Syndicate

The Associated Examining Board, EdExcel Foundation (London Examinations), the Midland Examining Group and the University of Cambridge Local Examinations Syndicate bear no responsibility for the example answers to questions taken from their past papers that are contained in this publication.

T3/T4

Advanced Modular Mathematics

FOREWORD This book is one of a series covering the University of London Examination and Assessment Council's modular 'A' level Mathematics syllabus. It covers all the subject material for Statistics 3 (Module T3) and Statistics 4 (T4). It also includes advice and guidance on tackling a statistics project, an important part of this course.

While this series of text books has been structured to match the University of London (ULEAC) syllabuses, we hope that the informal style of the text and approach to important concepts will encourage other readers, whose final examinations are from other examination Boards, to use the books for extra reading and practice.

This book is meant to be *used*; read the text, study the worked examples and work through the exercises, which will give you practice in the basic skills you need for maths at this level. There are many books for advanced mathematics, which include many more exercises: use this book to direct your studies, making use of as many other resources as you can. This book will act as a bridge between your new syllabus and the many older books that can still give even more practice in advanced mathematics.

Exercises are given at the end of each section; these range from the basic to exam-type questions. Many exercises, and worked examples, are based on *applications* of the mathematics in this book. We have given answers to all problems, so that you can check your work.

The National Extension College has more experience of flexible-learning materials than any other body (see p. ii). This series is a distillation of that experience: *Advanced Modular Mathematics* helps to put you in control of your own learning.

1

Further probability and Bayes' theorem

Section 1 continues the work of *Statistics 2* into more advanced ideas of probability theory up to the important theorem of Bayes. By the end of this section you should be able to:

● understand the ideas of independent events and conditional probability

● understand the total probability rule

● be able to use Bayes' theorem in simple examples.

Conditional probability and independence

We have already used the formula for conditional probability. If A and B are events in a sample space S then:

$$P(A \mid B) = \frac{P(A \cap B)}{P(B)}$$

The concept of independence of events was also introduced.

$$A \text{ is independent of } B \text{ if } P(A \mid B) = P(A)$$

This formula encapsulates the idea that A is independent of B if the probability of A is unaffected by the extra knowledge that B has occurred.

Events A and B for which $P(A \mid B) \neq P(A)$ are called dependent events.

Combining the formulae above it is not difficult to see that A is independent of B if and only if

$$P(A) = \frac{P(A \cap B)}{P(B)}$$

We therefore have the result that:

1

> A is independent of B if, and only if, $P(A \cap B) = P(A)P(B)$

This so-called product rule for probabilities applies only in circumstances where A is independent of B. It is usually the most useful rule for determining whether events are independent or not.

The symmetry of the formula suggests that if A is independent of B then the reverse is also true, so B is independent of A. This result is not difficult to prove.

Example

For events A, B in a sample space S show that A is independent of B implies B is independent of A.

Solution

A is independent of B $\Rightarrow P(A \mid B) = P(A)$ (by definition)

(We can use the symbol $\Rightarrow$ to mean 'implies'.)

$$\Rightarrow \frac{P(A \cap B)}{P(B)} = P(A) \qquad \text{(definition of } P(A \mid B))$$

$$\Rightarrow P(A \cap B) = P(A)P(B)$$

$$\Rightarrow \frac{P(B \cap A)}{P(A)} = P(B) \qquad \text{(using the result } A \cap B = B \cap A)$$

$$\Rightarrow P(B \mid A) = P(B)$$

$$\Rightarrow B \text{ is independent of } A.$$

This important result allows us to refer to 'independent events A and B' rather than using statements like 'A is independent of B', since the statements have been proved effectively equivalent.

If A and B are independent events then the following combinations are also independent:

- A and $\bar{B}$

- $\bar{A}$ and B

- $\bar{A}$ and $\bar{B}$

where $\bar{A}$ is the complement of the event A (or 'not A').

(Note that A and $\bar{A}$ are dependent events since if we know that A has occurred then $\bar{A}$ cannot have occurred and vice versa.)

The proof of these results is slightly more involved. To give a flavour of how the proofs work we will show the first.

Example	If A and B are independent events from a sample space S show that A and $\bar{B}$ are also independent.

Solution	A and B are independent

$$\Rightarrow \quad P(A \mid B) \quad = P(A)$$

$$\Rightarrow \quad P(A \cap B) \quad = P(A)P(B)$$

$$\Rightarrow \quad P(A \cap B) \quad = P(A)(1 - P(\bar{B}))$$

$$\Rightarrow \quad P(A \cap B) \quad = P(A) - P(A)P(\bar{B})$$

$$\Rightarrow \quad P(A)P(\bar{B}) \quad = P(A) - P(A \cap B)$$

$$\Rightarrow \quad P(A)P(\bar{B}) \quad = P(A \cap \bar{B}) \dots *$$

$$\Rightarrow \quad P(A) \quad = \frac{P(A \cap \bar{B})}{P(\bar{B})}$$

$$\Rightarrow \quad P(A) \quad = P(A \mid \bar{B})$$

$$\Rightarrow \quad A \text{ and } \bar{B} \text{ are independent.}$$

(The step * uses the result that

$$P(A) - P(A \cap B) = P(A \cap \bar{B})$$

which is easily seen to be true from a Venn diagram.)

The formulae

$$P(A \mid B) \quad = \frac{P(A \cap B)}{P(B)}$$

and $\quad P(B \mid A) \quad = \dfrac{P(B \cap A)}{P(A)}$

can be combined using the fact that $P(A \cap B) = P(B \cap A)$

to give $P(A \mid B)P(B) = P(B \mid A)P(A)$

or

$$P(A \mid B) = \frac{P(B \mid A)\,P(A)}{P(B)}$$

The following example shows how to work with conditional probabilities.

Cartons are filled with capsules. A machine checks that each contains the correct number of capsules and displays a flashing light if a carton does not contain the correct number of capsules. The machine is faulty. The probability that the light flashes when checking a correctly filled carton is 0.05 and the probability that it does not flash when checking an incorrectly filled carton is 0.06.

The probability that a carton is correctly filled is 0.90.

The light flashes when the machine is checking a randomly chosen carton. Find the probability that the carton is incorrectly filled.

[ULEAC SpecimenPaper T3]

Solution

Let C be the event 'a carton is correctly filled'

L be the event 'the light flashes'.

Then we are told

$$P(L \mid C) = 0.05$$
$$P(\bar{L} \mid \bar{C}) = 0.06$$
$$P(C) = 0.90$$

and we are asked to find $P(\bar{C} \mid L)$.

A natural approach to solving a problem where there are basically only two or three events is to use a tree diagram, and this is the method we will use here.

(For more events, other methods need to be developed.)

The complete diagram is:

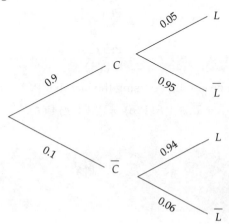

The numbers for $P(\bar{L} \mid C) = 0.95$ and $P(L \mid \bar{C}) = 0.94$ have been calculated using the obvious fact that if a carton is correctly filled then either the light flashes or it doesn't, so the two probabilities must add up to one. Similarly on the other branch.

Now $\quad P(\bar{C} \mid L) \quad = \quad \dfrac{P(\bar{C} \cap L)}{P(L)}$

$$= \dfrac{0.1 \times 0.94}{(0.9)\,(0.05) + (0.1)\,(0.94)}$$

(where the denominator is obtained by considering the two ways in which the light can flash)

$$= 0.6763 \quad (4\ \text{d.p.})$$

A Venn diagram (Figure 1.1) shows that $P(L) = P(C \cap L) + P(\bar{C} \cap L)$.

Figure 1.1

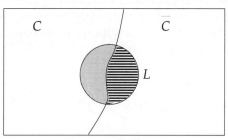

The probability of *L* is obtained by adding its respective intersections
with *C* and $\bar{C}$

Now the above result follows by replacing

$\qquad P(C \cap L)$ by $P(C)\,P(L \mid C)$

and $\qquad P(\bar{C} \cap L)$ by $P(\bar{C})\,P(L \mid \bar{C})$

From the previous solution we can note the following rule:

$$P(L) = P(C)\,P(L \mid C) + P(\bar{C})\,P(L \mid \bar{C})$$

You should now be able to complete Exercises 1–6 on pp. 10–12.

Law of total probability

The previous result is a particular case of a more general one.

Suppose S is a sample space and $A_1, A_2 \ldots A_n$ are events in S with the following properties:

5

$$A_i \cap A_j = \phi \quad \text{for each pair } i, j \text{ with } i \neq j$$

(or equivalently $P(A_i \cap A_j) = 0$)

and that

$$A_1 \cup A_2 \cup \ldots \cup A_n = S$$

(or equivalently $P(A_1 \cup A_2 \cup \ldots \cup A_n) = 1$).

The events $A_1, A_2 \ldots A_n$ are then pairwise mutually exclusive (by the first property) and exhaustive (by the second property). This means that they divide up the sample space completely and in a non-overlapping way (technically, they *partition S*).

Then if B is *any* other event in S it is the case that

$$P(B) = P(B \cap A_1) + P(B \cap A_2) + \ldots + P(B \cap A_n)$$

This result follows by extension from Figure 1.1 on p. 5. As before, we can replace each of the individual terms in this expression by its equivalent using the rule for conditional probability:

e.g. $P(B \cap A_1) = P(B \mid A_1) P(A_1)$

leading to

$$P(B) = P(B \mid A_1) P(A_1) + P(B \mid A_2) P(A_2) + \ldots + P(B \mid A_n) P(A_n)$$

i.e.

$$P(B) = \sum_{i=1}^{n} P(B \mid A_i) P(A_i)$$

where $A_1, \ldots A_n$ is a partition of S

This result is called the *Law of total probability*. You are unlikely to need it in this form in the examination. For the case of a sample space S which is partitioned by the events A_1, A_2, A_3 the result would reduce to

$$P(B) = P(B \mid A_1) P(A_1) + P(B \mid A_2) P(A_2) + P(B \mid A_3) P(A_3)$$

and correspondingly for the division into two events the result would reduce to

$$P(B) = P(B \mid A_1) P(A_1) + P(B \mid A_2) P(A_2)$$

which we have already seen in use (p. 5).

Useful as these formulae are for more advanced applications of the subject, you are unlikely to need them in an 'A' level examination. Problems which could be solved by using them can often be solved more easily by considering a tree diagram or a Venn diagram.

Figure 1.2 shows the connection between the law of total probability and a tree diagram in the case of a partition consisting of just two sets (A and $\bar A$).

Figure 1.2

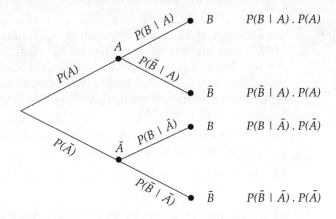

It can be seen that

$$P(B) = P(B \mid A)\, P(A) + P(B \mid \bar A)\, P(\bar A)$$

This is the law of total probability for a simple partition of a sample space into A and $\bar A$.

Bayes' theorem

The law of total probability leads directly to a statement of Bayes' theorem.

For simplicity we will consider the case where the sample space S is partitioned by just two events, A and $\bar A$. (Recall that $A \cup \bar A = S$ and $A \cap \bar A = \phi$ as required.)

If B is any other event in S then we know from p. 1 that

$$P(A \mid B) = \frac{P(A \cap B)}{P(B)}$$

We know from the law of total probability that

$$P(B) = P(B \mid A)\, P(A) + P(B \mid \bar A)\, P(\bar A)$$

and from p. 3 that

$$P(A \cap B) = P(A)\, P(B \mid A)$$

Combining these formulae gives

$$P(A \mid B) = \frac{P(A)\, P(B \mid A)}{P(A)\, P(B \mid A) + P(\bar A)\, P(B \mid \bar A)}$$

which is Bayes' theorem for a sample space partitioned by A and $\bar{A}$.

The following example from medical diagnostics illustrates how this rule might be used in a practical situation.

Example   It is known that the probability that an individual carries a certain virus is 0.002. Trials have shown that a test for the virus is not 100% reliable but that it will give a positive result if the virus is being carried, with probability 0.995, and that it will give a positive result if the virus is not being carried, with probability 0.001.

(a)   A certain individual gives a positive result to the test. Find the probability that he is carrying the virus.

(b)   Another individual gives a positive result. Find the probability that she is not carrying the virus.

(c)   Given that somebody gives a negative result to the test, find the probability that he is actually carrying the virus (i.e. that he will go undetected by the test).

Solution   The partition in this example is the events

$$V \quad = \text{carrying the virus}$$

$$\bar{V} \quad = \text{not carrying the virus}$$

since only one or other of these can be the case.

$$B \quad = \text{gives a positive result to the test}$$

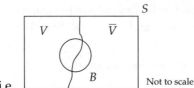

i.e.   Not to scale

The information in the question is now summarised as

$$P(V) \ = \ 0.002$$

$$P(\bar{V}) \ = \ 0.998$$

$$P(B \mid V) \ \ = \ 0.995$$

$$P(B \mid \bar{V}) \ \ = \ 0.001$$

(a)   To find $P(V \mid B)$

we use the formula

$$P(V \mid B) = \frac{(0.002)\,(0.995)}{(0.002)\,(0.995) + (0.001)\,(0.998)} = 0.6660 \quad (4\text{ d.p.})$$

(b)   Here we require $P(\bar{V} \mid B)$.

In the formula $P(\bar{V} \mid B) = \dfrac{P(\bar{V})\,P(B \mid \bar{V})}{P(B \mid \bar{V})\,P(\bar{V}) + P(B \mid V)\,P(V)}$

we have

$$P(\bar{V} \mid B) = \frac{(0.998)\,(0.001)}{(0.998)\,(0.001) + (0.995)\,(0.002)}$$

$$= 0.3340 \quad (4\text{ d.p.})$$

This is what we would expect: if a positive result is obtained, the individual is either carrying or not carrying the virus. So we could have obtained this answer from $1 - 0.666$.

(c)   We need to find $P(V \mid \bar{B})$.

By direct translation into the formula

$$P(V \mid \bar{B}) = \frac{P(V)\,P(\bar{B} \mid V)}{P(\bar{B} \mid V)\,P(V) + P(\bar{B} \mid \bar{V})\,P(\bar{V})}$$

$$= \frac{(0.002)\,(1 - 0.995)}{(1 - 0.995)\,(0.002) + (1 - 0.001)\,(0.998)}$$

$$= 0.00001 \quad (5\text{ d.p.})$$

This is a key result for the test – only 1 in 100,000 cases will go undetected on average. The previous results suggest, though, that patients who give positive results to this test should be subjected to further tests before firm conclusions about their status are drawn.

The result of p. 7 can be extended to a partition of S by n events $A_1, A_2, \dots A_n$ as

$$P(A_j \mid B) = \frac{P(A_j)\,P(B \mid A_j)}{P(B \mid A_1)\,P(A_1) + P(B \mid A_2)\,P(A_2) + \dots + P(B \mid A_n)\,P(A_n)}$$

or, using the Σ notation in the denominator, as

$$P(A_j \mid B) = \frac{P(A_j)\,P(B \mid A_j)}{\displaystyle\sum_{i=1}^{n} P(A_i)\,P(B \mid A_i)}$$

which is the form given in the ULEAC *Formula Book*.

When using this formula in examples it is a good idea to write it out in its expanded form first, after deciding how many events partition the sample space. This will usually be two or three events. The formula given in the handbook is simply a reminder of the structure of the formula.

Remember that you can also use tree diagrams and Venn diagrams to help see your way into a problem.

You should now be able to complete Exercises 7, 8 and 9 on pp. 12 and 13.

EXERCISES

1 Two machines I and II produce the same articles. Machine II produces twice as many articles as machine I. The probability that machine I produces a defective article is p and the corresponding probability for machine II is q. An article is drawn at random from the combined output of the machines and is found to be defective.

Find an expression for the probability that the article was produced on machine I.

[ULEAC 1993]

2 In a factory machines A, B and C are all producing springs of the same length. Of the production of springs in the factory, machine A produces 35% and machines B and C produce 25% and 40% respectively. Of their total production, machines A, B and C produce 3%, 6% and 5% defective springs respectively.

(a) Find the probability that
   (i)   a randomly selected spring is produced by machine A and is defective
   (ii) a randomly selected spring is defective.

(b) Given that a random selected spring is defective, find the probability that it was produced by machine C.

(c) Given that a randomly selected spring is not defective, find the probability that it was produced by either machine A or machine B.

[ULEAC 1994]

3 A bicycle shop stocks racing, touring and mountain bicycles. The following table shows the number of bicycles of each type in stock, together with their price range.

	Price range		
	< £250	£250 – £500	> £500
Racing	10	18	22
Touring	36	22	12
Mountain	28	32	20

A bicycle is selected at random for testing.

R is the event that a racing bicycle is selected.

S is the event that a bicycle worth between £250 and £500 is selected.

T is the event that a touring bicycle is selected.

($\bar{R}, \bar{S}, \bar{T}$ are the events not R, not S, not T respectively.)

(a) Write down the values of
  (i) $P(S)$
  (ii) $P(R \cap S)$
  (iii) $P(\bar{T} \cup \bar{S})$
  (iv) $P(S \mid R)$.

(b) Express in terms of the events that have been defined the event that a mountain bicycle is selected.

(c) Write down one of the events R, S or T which is
  (i)   mutually exclusive of R
  (ii) independent of S
  (iii) not independent of S.

  In each case justify your answer.

(d) Of the racing bicycles, 10% are blue, as are 40% of the touring bicycles and 20% of the mountain bicycles. What is the probability that a bicycle selected at random will be
  (i)   blue
  (ii) a mountain bicycle, given that it is blue?

[AEB 1995]

4 A and B are two events in a sample space S. Given that $P(A) = 0.32$, $P(B) = 0.5$ and $P(A \cup B) = 0.55$, find

(a) $P(A \cap B)$

(b) $P(\bar{A} \mid B)$

(c) $P(A \mid \bar{B})$.

5 Prove that if A and B are independent events from a sample space S then so are $\bar{A}$ and $\bar{B}$.

6 (a) A student has a fair coin and two six-sided dice, one of which is white and the other one blue. The student tosses the coin and then rolls both dice. Let X be a random variable such that if the coin falls heads, X is the sum of the scores on the two dice, otherwise X is the score on the white die only.

Find the probability function of X in the form of a table of possible values of X and their associated probabilities.

Find $P(3 \leq X \leq 7)$.

State the assumption you made to enable you to evaluate the probability function.

(b) The results of a traffic survey of the colour and type of car are given in the following table.

	Saloon	Estate
White	68	62
Green	26	32
Black	6	6

One car is selected at random from this group.

Find the probability that the selected car is

(i)   a green estate car

(ii)   a saloon car

(iii) a white car, given that it is not a saloon car.

Let W and G denote the events that the selected car is white and green respectively and let S be the event that the car is a saloon. Show that the event $W \cup G$ is independent of the event S.

Show, however, that the colour and type of car are not independent.

[AEB 1991]

7 In a certain country, the courts can reach one of three verdicts: 'guilty', 'not guilty' and 'not proven'. Records show that the probabilities of each of these verdicts are 0.75, 0.15 and 0.10 respectively.

It is also known that when a 'guilty' verdict is recorded there is a probability of 0.06 that the accused person is actually innocent. Similarly, if a 'not guilty' verdict is recorded the probability that the accused is in fact innocent in 0.93. If a 'not proven' verdict is reached the probability that the accused is innocent is 0.30.

Find

(a) the probability that an accused person is innocent

(b) the probability that an innocent person will be found guilty.

Comment on the system of justice in this country.

8 A diagnostic test for a particular disease known to affect one person in 500 is considered to be reasonably reliable. If a person suffers from the disease the test will give a positive result in 98% of cases. If a person is free of the disease a positive result will be recorded in only 3% of cases.

(a) Find the percentage of patients who give a positive result for this diagnostic test.

(b) What percentage giving a positive test result are actually suffering from the disease? Comment on your answer.

(c) Given that a person gives a negative result to the test, what is the probability that she has the disease (i.e. find the risk of a person not being picked up by the test).

9 In a multiple-choice examination each question has five possible answers. A certain student knows the answer to a particular question with probability p and if he doesn't know he guesses.

Given that he answered a particular question correctly, find the probability that he actually knew the answer to it. Give an interpretation of your answer when $p = \frac{1}{6}$.

SUMMARY   When you have finished this section, you should be able to solve probability problems involving

- conditional probability and independent events
- the law of total probability
- Bayes' theorem.

2

Further hypothesis testing

INTRODUCTION   This section extends the work of *Statistics 2* into more advanced ideas concerning statistical inference.

By the end of this section you should be able to:

● use *t*-tables

● conduct a hypothesis test for the mean of a normal distribution where the population variance is unknown

● find a confidence interval for the mean of a normal distribution with unknown variance

● conduct a hypothesis test for the variance of a normal distribution

● find a confidence interval for the variance of a normal distribution using the χ^2-distribution

● be able to determine the quality of an estimator by calculating its expectation and variance

● understand the concepts of Type I and Type II errors and be able to calculate the size and power of a test.

Testing the mean of a normal distribution when the population variance is unknown

So far, we have tested the mean of a normal distribution when the population variance is known. In circumstances where the population variance is not known, we are forced to use an estimated value. When we know σ^2 we can use the test statistic

$$z = \frac{\overline{X} - \mu}{(\sigma/\sqrt{n})}$$

which has the distribution N(0,1).

When, in this formula, we replace σ by s (i.e. an *estimate* of its value calculated from the data), the nature of the distribution changes.

The statistic $t = \dfrac{\bar{X} - \mu}{(s/\sqrt{n})}$ has the t-distribution with $n - 1$ degrees of freedom

We write

$$\frac{\bar{X} - \mu}{(s/\sqrt{n})} \sim t_{n-1}$$

The t-distribution is really a family of distributions, each symmetrical about zero. The phrase 'a t-distribution with v degrees of freedom' is often used. For our purposes the value of v is equal to $n - 1$, where n is the size of the sample used to calculate s^2.

As the sample size increases the shape of the t-distribution tends to the distribution $N(0,1)$. This is what we would expect since as n increases, s^2 approaches the true value of σ^2.

The 'A' level syllabus does not require you to understand the theory behind this result, but you do need to know the circumstances in which to apply the test and how to use the t-tables (pp. 234–5) correctly.

The following example illustrates how to conduct a two-tailed t-test, and in particular how to use the tables to find a critical region.

Example

A machine produces screws which have a length known to have a normal distribution with mean length 24 mm. After a routine servicing of the machine, a random sample of screws is taken and their lengths measured, giving the results (to 1 d.p.):

24.2, 24.1, 24.0, 23.9, 23.9, 23.8, 24.2, 24.3, 24.1, 24.0, 24.2

Is there sufficient evidence that the servicing of the machine has altered the mean length of screws?

Solution

We note first that the background population has a normal distribution and that no value for the population variance is given (indeed, the variance may have been altered by the servicing of the machine). These are precisely the circumstances in which the t-test is appropriate.

Calculation gives

$$\Sigma x_i = 264.7 \qquad \Sigma x_i^2 = 6369.89$$
$$n = 11$$

and hence

$$\bar{x} = \frac{264.7}{11} = 24.0636 \text{ (4 d.p.)}$$

$$s^2 = \frac{11}{10} \left(\frac{6369.89}{11} - 24.0636^2 \right)$$

$$= 0.0245 \quad \text{(4 d.p.)}$$

The test is set up as follows:

$$H_0: \mu = 24$$

$$H_1: \mu \neq 24 \quad \text{(a two-tailed test as we are looking for } a \text{ } change \text{ in } \mu\text{)}$$

Significance level 5%

Under H_0 the distribution of $\dfrac{\bar{x} - \mu}{(s/\sqrt{n})}$ is t_{10}

(Note that the number of degrees of freedom, v, is one less than the sample size.)

The calculated value of t is

$$\frac{24.0636 - 24}{0.1567/\sqrt{11}} = 1.3472 \quad \text{(4 d.p.)}$$

Turning to the tables on p. 234, the first column headed v gives the degrees of freedom of the test.

The columns headed 0.10, 0.05, 0.025, 0.01 and 0.005 are, for our purposes, concerned with the significance level of the test. Which of these we use will depend on the nature of the test (one-tailed or two-tailed) and the significance level we are using. An important property of the t-distribution is that it is symmetrical about zero (in just the same way that $N(0,1)$ is).

If we are conducting a two-tailed test at the 5% significance level, as in this example, we need $2\frac{1}{2}$% probability at either end to give our 5% critical region.

We will find our critical value under the column headed 0.025, giving the values 2.228 and symmetrically -2.228 (see Figure 2.1).

Figure 2.1

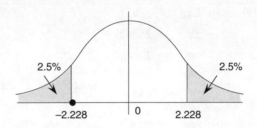

Critical regions for a two-tailed *t*-test at the 5% significance level

The interpretation of the value 2.228 is that for this particular *t*-distribution (t_{10})

$$P(t > 2.228) = 0.025 \text{ (from tables)}$$

and therefore by symmetry

$$P(t < -2.228) = 0.025$$

and consequently

$$P(-2.228 < t < 2.228) = 0.95$$

This means that we are correctly conducting a two-tailed test at the 5% significance level.

Now since our calculated *t*-value is less than the tabulated *t*-value $(1.3472 < 2.228)$ we have no reason, given the observed data, to reject H_0.

We can conclude that this is a perfectly reasonable sample to expect from a distribution $N(24,\sigma^2)$ at a 5% level of significance.

As a further exercise in using the tables, would it be a reasonable sample to expect at a 10% level of significance?

Yes, because the *t*-value from the tables is 1.812 and our test statistic is still less than this value.

The next example illustrates the use of the *t*-distribution for conducting a one-tailed test on the mean of a normal distribution.

Example   Analysis of waiting times in a doctor's surgery has shown that they are normally distributed with mean 472 secs. A new system of appointments is introduced and the following random sample of times is subsequently recorded:

450, 482, 375, 481, 432, 425, 404, 490, 411, 475, 477, 416, 463

Is there evidence at (a) 5% level, and (b) 1% level, that there has been a reduction in waiting times as a result of introducing the new system?

Solution	(a)

$$\Sigma x_i = 5781$$

$$\Sigma x_i^2 = 2586875$$

$$n = 13$$

$$\Rightarrow \quad \bar{x} = \frac{5781}{13} = 444.6923 \quad (4 \text{ d.p.})$$

$$s^2 = \frac{13}{12}\left(\frac{2586875}{13} - 444.6923^2\right)$$

$$= 1342.3974 \quad (4 \text{ d.p.})$$

H_0: $\mu = 472$

H_1: $\mu < 472$ (one-tailed test as we are testing for a reduction in waiting times)

Significance level 5%

Under H_0 the distribution of $\dfrac{\bar{X} - \mu}{(s/\sqrt{n})}$ is t_{12} (since $n = 13$).

The calculated value of t is

$$t = \frac{444.6923 - 472}{36.6387/\sqrt{13}}$$

$$= -2.6873 \quad (4 \text{ d.p.})$$

Now in order to find the critical region we need to find from the tables (p. 234) the value of $-t_0$, shown in Figure 2.2.

Figure 2.2	

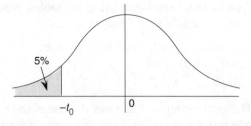

5%

$-t_0$ 0

Finding the critical point for a one-tailed t-test at the 5% significance level

Using the symmetry of the curve, the value we will find from the tables will be t_0, as shown in Figure 2.3. In order to find this value we need to use the column headed 0.05.

Figure 2.3

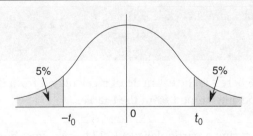

The values of *t* for a two-tailed *t*-test at the 10% significance level

Following this down to $\nu = 12$ we find the value 1.782. Therefore our critical value $-t_0$ is -1.782.

Since the calculated value (-2.6873) is less than the tabulated value (-1.782) we are in the critical region. We therefore reject the null hypothesis and conclude that, at the 5% level of significance, there is evidence to suggest that waiting times have been reduced.

(b) For a test at the 1% significance level all of the calculations remain the same but the critical value is found in the column headed 0.01 at $\nu = 12$ and is -2.681.

Since $-2.6873 < -2.681$ we have to conclude that at the 1% level of significance there is evidence of a reduction in waiting times. We would therefore accept H_1 at this level of significance.

Calculating a confidence interval for the mean of a normal distribution when the population variance is unknown

In *Statistics 2*, Section 2 we saw how to calculate a 95% confidence interval for μ, the population mean of a normal distribution, by using the formula

$$\bar{x} \pm 1.96 \; \frac{\sigma}{\sqrt{n}} \hspace{3cm} \text{(Statistics 2, p. 19)}$$

and we stated that we could be 95% certain that this interval (dependent on the values of $\bar{x}$, σ, n) contained the true value of μ.

When the value of σ is not known then we have to use an estimate for its value. As a consequence of this, we have to use the *t*-tables to find the size of the interval. Our interval now takes the form

$$\bar{x} \pm t_0 \frac{s}{\sqrt{n}}$$

where s is the estimate of σ calculated from the sample and t_0 is a value to be determined from the t-tables.

Example

During a particular week, 13 babies were born in a maternity unit. Part of the standard procedure is to measure the length of the baby. Given below is a list of the lengths in centimetres of the babies born in this particular week

49	50	45	51	47	49	48
54	53	55	45	50	48	

Assuming that this sample comes from an underlying normal population, calculate a 95% confidence interval for the mean of the population.

[AEB 1980]

Solution

$$\Sigma x_i = 644$$

$$\Sigma x_i^2 = 32020$$

$$n = 13$$

$$\Rightarrow \quad \bar{x} = 49.5385 \quad \text{(4 d.p.)}$$

$$s^2 = \frac{13}{12}\left(\frac{32020}{13} - 49.5385^2\right)$$

$$= 9.7692 \quad \text{(4 d.p.)}$$

From the tables in the column headed 0.025 we find $t_{12} = 2.179$.

The interval is therefore

$$49.5385 \pm 2.179 \times \frac{3.1256}{\sqrt{13}}$$

$$= (47.65,\ 51.43)$$

This interval therefore contains the true value of μ with 95% confidence.

In every example we have looked at where it has been necessary to use the t-distribution, an essential requirement was that the background population had a normal distribution. From our work in *Statistics 2*, however, we know that if the sample size is large enough, we can make use of the central limit theorem, namely that

$$\bar{X} \sim N\left(\mu, \frac{\sigma^2}{n}\right)$$

This result applies whatever the background distribution happens to be (we do not even have to know what it is). We can use this result to find confidence intervals, as the following example shows.

Example

A sample of size 30 gave the following values:

$$s^2 = 3.74 \qquad \bar{x} = 41.4$$

Find a 98% confidence interval for the mean of the population.

Solution

According to the central limit theorem

$$\bar{X} \sim N\left(\mu, \frac{\sigma^2}{n}\right)$$

but in this instance we do not have a value for σ^2. However, we do have an estimate for its value, namely $s^2 = 3.74$.

We can therefore say that $\bar{X}$ is approximately $N\left(\mu, \frac{3.74}{30}\right)$.

This gives $\bar{X}$ to be approximately $N(\mu, 0.3531^2)$.

Now, because we have used an estimate for σ^2 we need to use the t-distribution to find the confidence interval.

It will be

$$41.4 \pm t_0 (0.3531)$$

where the value of t_0 is found on p.234 at $v = 29$ and in the column headed 0.01 (since for a 98% interval we need 1% of the probability at each end). We find $t_0 = 2.462$.

The interval is therefore:

$$41.4 \pm (2.462)(0.3531)$$
$$= 41.4 \pm 0.8693$$
$$= (40.53, 42.27)$$

You should now be able to complete Exercises 1–4 on pp. 35–6.

Hypothesis test for the variance of a normal distribution

When testing the mean of a normal distribution we have used (without proof) the properties that

$$z = \frac{\bar{x} - \mu}{\sigma/\sqrt{n}} \sim N(0,1) \quad \text{or} \quad t = \frac{\bar{x} - \mu}{s/\sqrt{n}} \sim t_{n-1}$$

depending on whether we know σ or not. Now we consider a result which enables us to conduct hypothesis tests on the variance of a normal distribution.

If $x_1, x_2, x_3, \ldots x_n$ is a sample of size n from a distribution $N(\mu, \sigma^2)$ then

$$\frac{(n-1)s^2}{\sigma^2} \sim \chi^2(n-1)$$

where $\chi^2(n-1)$ is a chi-squared distribution with $n-1$ degrees of freedom. This is exactly the distribution we met in *Statistics 2*, Section 4. As in that section, the theory behind this result is not required. However, you could be asked to use this result to test hypotheses concerning σ^2. This section is concerned with hypothesis tests and the next section deals with confidence intervals. Both sections depend on the above result.

Example

The amount of a precious metal extracted from one tonne of ore has a normal distribution with mean 27.2 grams and variance 2.2 grams. A new source of the ore is discovered and successive samples give the following amount of metal per tonne:

16.91　　17.23　　14.14　　17.32　　18.25　　19.41　　15.82　　18.47　　16.81

Is there any evidence that samples from the new source are of different variability?

(We need to test the variance to see if it has changed.)

Solution

Calculation gives
$$\Sigma x_i = 154.36$$
$$\Sigma x_i^2 = 2666.5430$$
$$n = 9$$

and hence
$$\bar{x} = 17.1511 \ (4 \text{ d.p.})$$
$$s^2 = 2.3872 \ (4 \text{ d.p.})$$

$$H_0: \sigma^2 = 2.2$$

H_1: $\sigma^2 \neq 2.2$ (two-tailed since we are looking for a change in σ^2 rather than an increase or decrease)

5% significance level.

The test statistic is $\dfrac{(n-1)\,s^2}{\sigma^2} = \dfrac{8 \times 2.3872}{2.2} = 8.6807$

Under H_0 and according to the above result this comes from a $\chi^2(8)$ distribution.

Turning now to the χ^2-tables on p. 230, we see that under $v = 8$ and reading along at the points 0.975 and 0.025 (i.e. 2.5% at either end) the critical values are 2.180 and 17.535 respectively.

Our value for the test statistic is well within these two values, and so in this case we would accept H_0 and conclude that samples from the new source are not, at the 5% level, of different variability than those from the original source.

The next example illustrates a one-tailed test for variance.

Example

Under carefully controlled conditions the germination times for a certain variety of pea seed follow a normal distribution with mean 34.23 hours and variance 0.14 hours. In less controlled conditions a sample of 10 seeds gave the following times for germination:

| 36.15 | 37.92 | 37.45 | 36.81 | 36.93 | 37.18 | 36.94 | 37.18 |

37.24   37.38

Is there any evidence at the 5% level that the times of germination have become more variable under the less controlled conditions?

Solution

$\Sigma x_i = 371.18$

$\Sigma x_i^2 = 13779.4028$

$n = 10$

$\Rightarrow \bar{x} = 37.118$

$s^2 = 0.2160$

H_0: $\sigma^2 = 0.14$ hours

H_1: $\sigma^2 > 0.14$ hours   (testing for an increase in variance)

5% significance level

The test statistic is $\dfrac{(n-1)\,s^2}{\sigma^2} = \dfrac{8 \times 0.2160}{0.14}$ under H_0 = 12.3429   (4 d.p.)

From the χ^2-tables on p. 230 we see that for $v = 9$, in the vertical column under 0.050, $\chi^2(9) = 16.919$.

Our calculated value is less than this critical value. This means we can accept the null hypothesis and conclude that there is no evident increase in variability in germination times.

The next example tests for a decrease in variance. You will then have seen how to use the tables in all circumstances.

Example

The time for a certain chemical process to be completed has a normal distribution with mean 33.2 minutes and variance 1.12 minutes. In an attempt to make the process time less variable a new technique was applied to the process and the following times were recorded for 13 experiments:

33.4	33.3	31.8	32.4	31.5	34.6	33.5	33.9
34.2	33.3	34.2	32.4	31.9			

Is there evidence that the technique has reduced the variability of the experiment times at the 5% significance level?

Solution

$$\Sigma x_i = 430.4$$

$$\Sigma x_i^2 = 14261.86$$

$$n = 13$$

$$\Rightarrow \overline{x} = 33.1078 \quad \text{(4 d.p.)}$$

$$s^2 = \frac{13}{12}\left(\frac{14261.86}{13} - 33.1078^2\right)$$

$$= 1.0258 \quad \text{(4 d.p.)}$$

$$H_0: \sigma^2 = 1.12$$

$$H_1: \sigma^2 < 1.12 \quad \text{(testing for a decrease in variance)}$$

5% significance level

The test statistic is $\dfrac{(n-1)\,s^2}{\sigma^2}$ which under H_0 equals

$$\frac{12 \times 1.0258}{1.12} = 10.9904 \quad \text{(4 d.p.)}$$

From the χ^2-tables on p. 230 we see that for $v = 12$, in the vertical column under 0.95, $\chi^2(12) = 5.226$. This defines a critical region shown shaded in Figure 2.4.

Figure 2.4

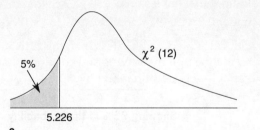

The curve of $\chi^2(12)$ showing a critical region for a 5% significance test

Since our calculated value of $\chi^2(12)$ is greater than the tabulated value, we accept H_0 at the 5% significance level. From the evidence of the sample we conclude that there has been no significant decrease in variability of process time.

Confidence intervals for the variance of a normal distribution

Just as we have constructed confidence intervals for the mean of a normal distribution we can do the same for the variance by using the χ^2-distribution.

The method is more involved than when we used the normal distribution or the t-distribution to find confidence intervals for μ. This is partly because the χ^2-distribution is not symmetric.

Example

Data from a known normal population are collected and a sample of size 20 gives a value of $s^2 = 8.92$. Find a 95% confidence interval for the population variance σ^2.

Solution

The following approach, including a diagram for clarification, is highly recommended for finding this type of confidence interval.

We know that $(n-1)\dfrac{s^2}{\sigma^2} \sim \chi^2(n-1)$ and we wish to find the values x_1 and x_2 shown in Figure 2.5.

Figure 2.5

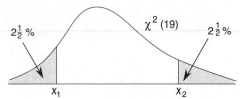

Showing 95% of the probability distribution of $\chi^2(19)$

The values x_1 and x_2 in the diagram have the required property that

$$P\left(x_1 < \frac{(n-1)\,s^2}{\sigma^2} < x_2\right) = 0.95$$

From the tables (p. 230) we have

$$P(\chi^2(19) > x_1) = 0.975 \Rightarrow x_1 = 8.907$$
$$P(\chi^2(19) > x_2) = 0.025 \Rightarrow x_2 = 32.852$$

Substituting all the known numbers into the expression above we obtain

$$P\left(8.907 < \frac{19 \times 8.92}{\sigma^2} < 32.852\right) = 0.95$$

Rearranging (solving the inequality for σ^2) gives

$$P\left(\frac{19 \times 8.92}{32.852} < \sigma^2 < \frac{19 \times 8.92}{8.907}\right) = 0.95$$

Finally, this gives the interval

$(5.16, 19.03)$ for σ^2.

The corresponding 95% confidence interval for the population standard deviation is obtained from this by taking the square root of these values, giving $(2.27, 4.36)$ as a 95% interval for σ.

Example A sample of 25 from a known normal population gives a value of 3.83 for s^2. Find 90% confidence limits for the population variance σ^2.

Solution Proceeding as before we require values of x_1 and x_2 shown in Figure 2.6.

Figure 2.6

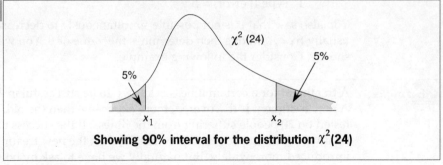

Showing 90% interval for the distribution $\chi^2(24)$

From the tables (p. 230)

$$P(\chi^2(24) > x_1) = 0.95 \Rightarrow x_1 = 13.848$$
$$P(\chi^2(24) > x_2) = 0.05 \Rightarrow x_2 = 36.415$$

giving the interval

$$P\left(13.848 < \frac{24 \times 3.83}{\sigma^2} < 36.415\right) = 0.90$$

$$\Rightarrow \quad P\left(\frac{24 \times 3.83}{36.415} < \sigma^2 < \frac{24 \times 3.83}{13.848}\right) = 0.90$$

giving the interval $(2.52, 6.64)$ for σ^2.

If required, the corresponding 90% confidence interval for σ would be obtained from this by

$$\left(\sqrt{2.52}, \ \sqrt{6.64}\right)$$

giving $(1.59, 2.58)$ for σ.

To test your understanding of tests and confidence intervals for the variance of a normal distribution you should now attempt Exercises 5 and 6 at the end of this section.

Errors in hypothesis testing – the size and power of a test

In *Statistics 2*, Section 3 you learned that the two types of error associated with hypothesis testing are defined as:

Type I   Reject H_0 when H_0 is true

Type II   Accept H_0 when H_0 is false

and that we write

$$P(\text{Type I error}) = \alpha$$

P(Type II error) = β

You also saw that it is not possible simultaneously to decrease α and β. We usually fix α, and this then determines the value of β. You will see how shortly. Consider the following example.

Example

A treatment for a certain illness is known to be successful in 70% of cases. A new treatment is discovered, more expensive than the old, which is tested on 20 people suffering from the illness. If the success rate of the new treatment is an improvement on the old, then the new treatment will be introduced more widely. But naturally we have to ask by how much the recovery rate should improve if we are to favour replacing the original treatment with the new, more expensive one.

Since 70% of 20 is 14, we would expect 14 of the patients to recover under the old treatment. Would we consider 15 patients recovering with the new treatment a significant improvement? Certainly we would have little hesitation about preferring the second treatment if all the patients recovered as a result of using it (although we may still be committing a Type I error). But round about 15, 16, 17 there is a region of uncertainty. This gradually decreases as we approach 20.

At some point we have to make a decision – to adopt a *decision rule* for this test. In the circumstances, it is probably advisable (considering the expense of the new compared with the original treatment) to minimise the probability of a Type I error – it would be an expensive mistake to accept H_1 if in fact H_0 were true.

Suppose the decision rule is:

'Accept that there is an improvement if 18 or more patients recover when given the new treatment.'

What is the *size* of the critical region for the test (i.e. α, the probability of making a Type I error)?

Solution

The hypotheses for the problem are:

H_0: $p \le 0.7$ (i.e. the new treatment is no different to the old)

H_1: $p > 0.7$ (a one-tailed test as we are looking for an increase in the probability of recovery)

The significance level of the test will be worked out from the decision rule in this case.

We reject H_0 if, for the distribution $X \sim B(20, 0.7)$ we obtain a result $X \ge 18$.

Now $P(X \ge 18) = \binom{20}{18}(0.7)^{18}(0.3)^{2}$

$$+ \binom{20}{19}(0.7)^{19}(0.3)$$

$$+ \binom{20}{20} (0.7)^{20}$$
$$= 0.0355$$

Therefore, using the given decision rule, the significance level for the test is 0.0355 or 3.55%. This also means that the probability of a Type I error is

$$\alpha = 0.0355.$$

The value of β is not as easily determined since it depends on the true value of the parameter (p in this example).

Example   Find the probability, in terms of p, of a Type II error for this test.

Solution   Suppose the null hypothesis is false, i.e. $p > 0.7$. Then to find the probability function we need to work out $P(X \leq 17)$, since it is in these circumstances that we will commit a Type II error.

$$P(X \leq 17) = 1 - P(X \geq 18)$$
$$= 1 - \binom{20}{18} p^{18} (1 - p)^2$$
$$- \binom{20}{19} p^{19} (1 - p) - \binom{20}{20} p^{20}$$

This simplifies to

$$1 - p^{18} \left[190(1 - p)^2 + 20p(1 - p) + p^2 \right]$$
$$\beta = 1 - p^{18} \left[171p^2 - 360p + 190 \right]$$

This expression, for values of $p > 0.7$, gives the probability of a Type II error, and is called the *operating characteristic* of the test.

When $p = 0.8$, for example, we get $\beta = 0.7939$

and $p = 0.9$ gives $\beta = 0.3231$

Thus the higher the true value of the parameter, the less likely we are wrongly to accept H_0.

The quantity $1 - \beta$ is a measure of the probability of rejecting H_0 when H_0 is false (i.e. of making a correct decision to reject H_0) and is called the *power of the test*.

In our example the power function is

$$p^{18} \left[171p^2 - 360p + 190 \right]$$

and from the calculations above, the power is

0.2061 when $p = 0.8$

0.6769 when $p = 0.9$

A graph of the power function is shown in Figure 2.7.

Figure 2.7

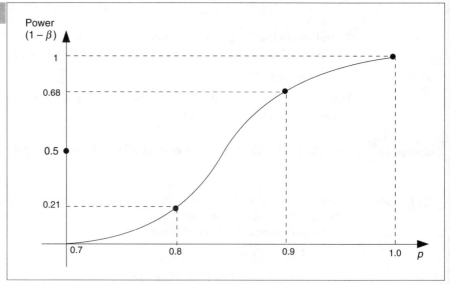

The steepness of the power curve measures how effectively and sensitively the test performs. A steep curve will mean that fairly small differences in p (or the parameter being tested in general) will result in large differences in $1 - \beta$ and therefore in β itself.

Consider the following example from a Poisson distribution.

Example

To test the null hypothesis $\mu = 2$ against the alternative hypothesis $\mu > 2$ for a known Poisson distribution, a single observation is taken. A decision rule for the hypothesis test is 'Accept H_0 if $X \leq 5$, otherwise reject H_0.'

Find the level of significance (α) for the test. Find an expression for the power of the test in terms of μ and sketch the graph of the power function.

Solution

$$H_0: \quad \mu = 2$$
$$H_1: \quad \mu > 2$$

To find α the significance level (or size of the critical region or, equivalently, the probability of a Type I error) we need to evaluate

$$P(X \geq 6 \mid \mu = 2)$$

$$\alpha = 1 - \left(e^{-2} + 2e^{-2} + \frac{2^2 e^{-2}}{2!} + \frac{2^3 e^{-2}}{3!} + \frac{2^4 e^{-2}}{4!} + \frac{2^5 e^{-2}}{5!} \right)$$

$$= 0.0166$$

(i.e. approximately 1.7% significance level).

The value of β is given by

$$\beta \;=\; P(X \le 5 \mid \mu > 2)$$

$$=\; e^{-\mu} + \mu e^{-\mu} + \frac{\mu^2}{2!}e^{-\mu} + \frac{\mu^3}{3!}e^{-\mu} + \frac{\mu^4}{4!}e^{-\mu} + \frac{\mu^5}{5!}e^{-\mu}$$

$$=\; e^{-\mu}\left[1 + \mu + \frac{\mu^2}{2} + \frac{\mu^3}{6} + \frac{\mu^4}{24} + \frac{\mu^5}{120}\right]$$

Consequently the power function is given by

$$1 - \beta \;=\; 1 - e^{-\mu}\left[1 + \mu + \frac{\mu^2}{2} + \frac{\mu^3}{6} + \frac{\mu^4}{24} + \frac{\mu^5}{120}\right]$$

e.g. $\mu = 3$ gives power = 0.0839
$\mu = 4$ gives power = 0.2149
$\mu = 5$ gives power = 0.3840

The graph is shown in Figure 2.8.

Figure 2.8

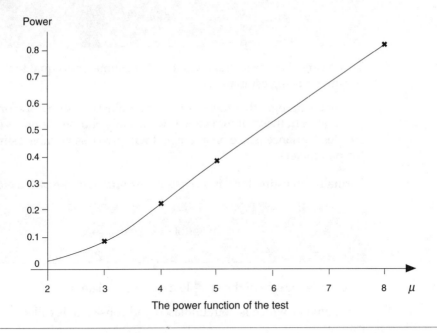

The power function of the test

You should now be able to answer Exercises 7 and 8 at the end of this section.

The quality of estimators

A statistic calculated from sample data is used to find an *estimate* of the corresponding population parameter. The statistics most commonly used for this are $\bar{x}$ and s^2. The statistic is called an *estimator* for the parameter and its calculated value for any particular sample is called an *estimate* (of the parameter).

e.g. $\bar{x}$ is used as an estimator for μ

s^2 is used as an estimator for σ^2.

These are good estimators in the sense that

$$E(\bar{x}) = \mu$$
$$E(s^2) = \sigma^2$$

Formally, an estimator $\hat{\theta}$ is an *unbiased* estimator of the parameter θ if

$$E(\hat{\theta}) = \theta$$

This means that the average value of the estimator is equal to the parameter being estimated.

It may be, though, that there are several unbiased estimators for a given parameter. In these circumstances we usually choose the one with the smallest variance (since on average it will give less variable estimates for the parameter).

Formally, an estimator $\hat{\theta}$ is a *consistent* estimator of the parameter θ if

$$Var(\hat{\theta}) \rightarrow 0 \text{ as } n \rightarrow \infty$$

where n is the size of the sample used to calculate $\hat{\theta}$.

An estimator which is both unbiased and consistent is called an *efficient* estimator.

Example	A health visitor measures the height of a large number of four-year-olds. Their mean height in centimetres is μ with a standard deviation of σ.

$\bar{X}$ is the mean height of a random sample of five children and $\bar{Y}$ is the mean height of a further independent random sample of n children.

(a) Find the mean and variance, in terms of μ and σ^2, of

   (i) $\bar{X}$

   (ii) $\dfrac{(\bar{X}+\bar{Y})}{2}$

   (iii) $\dfrac{(\bar{X}+n\bar{Y})}{(n+5)}$

   (iv) $\dfrac{(5\bar{X}+n\bar{Y})}{(n+5)}$

(b) The expressions in (ii), (iii) and (iv) above are all possible estimators of μ. For each expression say whether or not the estimator is

   (i)   unbiased

   (ii) consistent.

Solution

(a) (i) $E(\bar{X}) = E\left(\dfrac{X_1 + X_2 + X_3 + X_4 + X_5}{5}\right)$

$\qquad\qquad = \frac{1}{5}\left(E(X_1) + E(X_2) + E(X_3) + E(X_4) + E(X_5)\right)$

$\qquad\qquad = \frac{1}{5}\left(\mu + \mu + \mu + \mu + \mu\right)$

$\qquad\qquad = \mu$

$\qquad\quad \mathrm{Var}(\bar{X}) = \mathrm{Var}\left(\dfrac{X_1 + X_2 + X_3 + X_4 + X_5}{5}\right)$

$\qquad\qquad = \frac{1}{25}\left(\mathrm{Var}(X_1) + \mathrm{Var}(X_2) + \mathrm{Var}(X_3) + \mathrm{Var}(X_4) + \mathrm{Var}(X_5)\right)$

$\qquad\qquad = \frac{1}{25}\left(\sigma^2 + \sigma^2 + \sigma^2 + \sigma^2 + \sigma^2\right)$

$\qquad\qquad = \dfrac{\sigma^2}{5}$

(ii) $E\left(\dfrac{\bar{X}+\bar{Y}}{2}\right) = \frac{1}{2}E(\bar{X}) + \frac{1}{2}E(\bar{Y})$

$\qquad\qquad\qquad\quad = \frac{1}{2}\mu + \frac{1}{2}\mu$

$\qquad\qquad\qquad\quad = \mu$

$\qquad\quad \mathrm{Var}\left(\dfrac{\bar{X}+\bar{Y}}{2}\right) = \frac{1}{4}\mathrm{Var}(\bar{X}) + \frac{1}{4}\mathrm{Var}(\bar{Y})$

33

$$= \left(\tfrac{1}{4}\right)\left(\frac{\sigma^2}{5}\right) + \left(\tfrac{1}{4}\right)\left(\frac{\sigma^2}{n}\right)$$

$$= \frac{\sigma^2}{4}\left(\tfrac{1}{5} + \tfrac{1}{n}\right)$$

(iii) $\quad E\left(\dfrac{\bar{X} + n\bar{Y}}{n+5}\right) = \dfrac{1}{n+5}\left(E(\bar{X}) + nE(\bar{Y})\right)$

$$= \frac{1}{n+5}\left(\mu + n\mu\right)$$

$$= \left(\frac{n+1}{n+5}\right)\mu$$

$\quad\quad \mathrm{Var}\left(\dfrac{\bar{X} + n\bar{Y}}{n+5}\right) = \dfrac{1}{(n+5)^2}\left(\dfrac{\sigma^2}{5} + n^2 \cdot \dfrac{\sigma^2}{n}\right)$

$$= \frac{\sigma^2}{(n+5)^2}\left(\tfrac{1}{5} + n\right) = \frac{\sigma^2}{5}\left(\frac{1+5n}{(n+5)^2}\right)$$

(iv) $\quad E\left(\dfrac{5\bar{X} + n\bar{Y}}{n+5}\right) = \dfrac{1}{n+5}\left(5E(\bar{X}) + nE(\bar{Y})\right)$

$$= \frac{1}{n+5}\left(5\mu + n\mu\right)$$

$$= \mu$$

$\quad\quad \mathrm{Var}\left(\dfrac{5\bar{X} + n\bar{Y}}{n+5}\right) = \dfrac{1}{(n+5)^2}\left(25\,\mathrm{Var}(\bar{X}) + n^2\,\mathrm{Var}(\bar{Y})\right)$

$$= \frac{1}{(n+5)^2}\left(25\frac{\sigma^2}{5} + n^2\frac{\sigma^2}{n}\right)$$

$$= \frac{\sigma^2}{(n+5)^2}\left(5 + n\right)$$

$$= \frac{\sigma^2}{n+5}$$

(b) $\quad \dfrac{\bar{X} + \bar{Y}}{2}$ is unbiased and not consistent

$\quad$ since $E\left(\dfrac{\bar{X} + \bar{Y}}{2}\right) = \mu$

but $\mathrm{Var}\left(\dfrac{\bar{X}+\bar{Y}}{2}\right) \to \dfrac{\sigma^2}{20}$ as $n \to \infty$

$\dfrac{\bar{X}+n\bar{Y}}{n+5}$ is biased and consistent

since $\mathrm{E}\left(\dfrac{\bar{X}+n\bar{Y}}{n+5}\right) \neq \mu$

and $\mathrm{Var}\left(\dfrac{\bar{X}+n\bar{Y}}{n+5}\right) \to 0$ as $n \to \infty$

$\dfrac{5\bar{X}+n\bar{Y}}{n+5}$ is unbiased and consistent

since $\mathrm{E}\left(\dfrac{5\bar{X}+n\bar{Y}}{n+5}\right) = \mu$

and $\mathrm{Var}\left(\dfrac{5\bar{X}+n\bar{Y}}{n+5}\right) \to 0$ as $n \to \infty$

Of the three alternatives given in (ii), (iii) and (iv), therefore, the last of these is an efficient estimator for μ and would be the preferred choice.

You should now be able to complete Exercises 9 and 10 on pp. 37–8.

EXERCISES

1 A manufacturer claims that the lifetime of its batteries is normally distributed with mean 21.5 hours. A laboratory tests eight batteries and finds the lifetimes of these batteries to be as follows:

$$19.7 \quad 18.4 \quad 22.2 \quad 20.8 \quad 16.9 \quad 25.3 \quad 23.2 \quad 21.1$$

Stating clearly your hypotheses, examine whether or not these lifetimes indicate that the batteries have a shorter mean lifetime than that claimed by the company. Use a 5% level of significance.

[ULEAC 1996]

2 The following data are thought to come from a normal distribution with mean 30. Test this claim at the 5% level of significance.

28.8   31.2   30.4   29.5   26.7   32.4   29.8   29.5   32.1
28.6   29.4   31.0

3 Calculate a 98% confidence interval for the population mean of the following data, taken from a normal distribution.

73.6   78.4   75.2   73.9   77.1   78.0   76.5   73.8
74.2   76.4

4 It is thought that the data in Exercise 3 come from a normal distribution with $\mu = 74$. Test the hypothesis $H_0: \mu = 74$ against $H_1: \mu > 74$ at a 5% level of significance.

5 Students accepted on a course show a wide range of times for completing a certain task. Before the course starts, evidence suggests that the times in seconds for completing the task have a distribution $N(300, 6^2)$.

After spending two weeks on the course the students are re-tested and a sample of 15 students gave a value of 25.2 for the sample variance. Is there evidence at the 5% level of significance of a reduction in variability of times for the task?

What value of sample variance would provide such evidence?

6 A random sample of 14 cows was selected from a large dairy herd at Brookfield Farm. The milk yield in one week was recorded in kilograms for each cow. The results are given below.

169.6   142.0   103.3   111.6   123.4   143.5   155.1
101.7   170.7   113.2   130.9   146.1   169.3   155.5

Assuming that this sample came from an underlying normal population

(i)   calculate a 95% confidence interval for the variance of the population

(ii)   calculate a 95% confidence interval for the mean of the population

(iii)   calculate a second 95% interval for the mean of the population, where this time you should also assume that the variance equals 289.

Which of the intervals that you have calculated for the mean of the population is the more appropriate and why?

[AEB 1981]

7 A well-maintained machine is set so that it will produce cylindrical rods of diameter D mm, where $D \sim N(20, \sigma^2)$.

A random sample of 10 rods taken from the output of the machine resulted in unbiased estimates of the mean and the variance of the diameters of the rods of 20.6 mm and 0.83 mm respectively.

(a) Calculate a 95% confidence interval for the standard deviation of the population of diameters.

(b) Stating clearly your hypotheses, test whether or not the diameter of the rods has increased. Use a 5% level of significance.

(c) State a model you would regard as appropriate

    (i)   before the sample was selected

    (ii) after the analysis is completed.

[ULEAC Specimen paper T3]

8 (a) Define Type I and Type II errors. In the context of hypothesis testing, what is meant by

    (i)   size

    (ii) power?

(b) Two packers, A and B, fill boxes of matches. For packer A, the distribution of the number of matches put into each box is normal with mean 500 matches and standard deviation 5.3. For packer B, the distribution is normal with mean 504 and standard deviation 4.8. A batch of boxes has been filled by one packer, but the quality manager does not know which. Some substandard matches have been used by packer A, so the quality manager decides to test

    H_0: batch from packer A, against H_1: batch from packer B

by counting the contents of a random sample of six boxes. She will reject H_0 if the mean number of matches in the boxes is greater than a constant, k. Find k such that the risk of Type I error is 5%. What is the risk of Type II error?

(c) Carry out the test for a sample of six boxes with contents 511, 499, 500, 498, 507, 495 matches.

(d) She decides to increase the sample size and test again How many more boxes should she look at if the risk of Type I error is to stay 5%, but the risk of Type II error is to drop to just under 1%?

9 A single observation, x, is to be taken from a Poisson distribution with parameter μ. This observation is to be used to test H_0: $\mu \geq 6$ against H_1: $\mu < 6$. The critical region is chosen to be $x \leq 2$.

(a) Find the size of the critical region.

(b) Show that the power function for this test is given by

$$\frac{1}{2}e^{-\mu}(2 + 2\mu + \mu^2)$$

(c) The table below gives the values of the power function to two decimal places.

μ	1.0	1.5	2.0	4.0	5.0	6.0	7.0
Power	0.92	0.81	s	0.24	t	0.06	0.03

Calculate the values of s and t.

(d) Draw a graph of the power function.

(e) Find the range of values of μ for which the power of this test is greater than 0.8.

[ULEAC 1996]

10 (a) What is a consistent estimator?

(b) A large mail order firm wishes to estimate the mean value of the orders it receives. $\bar{X}$ denotes the mean value of a random sample of 10 orders selected by an employee and $\bar{Y}$ denotes the mean value of a further independent random sample of size n

(i) find the mean and variance of $T_1 = \dfrac{\bar{X} + \bar{Y}}{2}$ in terms of the population mean, μ, and variance, σ^2. Hence show that T_1 is an unbiased but not a consistent estimator of μ.

(ii) show that $T_2 = \dfrac{\bar{X} + n\bar{Y}}{n+1}$ is a consistent estimator of μ.

(iii) write down another consistent estimator of μ which has a smaller variance than T_2 for large n.

(Hint: regard all $n + 10$ observations as one sample.)

[AEB 1985]

<table>
<tr><td>SUMMARY</td><td>By the end of this section you should be able to:</td></tr>
</table>

- test the mean of a normal distribution when σ^2 is unknown using a *t*-test.

- test the variance of a normal distribution using the χ^2-distribution

- find confidence intervals for the mean and variance of a normal distribution using *t*-tables and χ^2-tables respectively

- calculate the size and power of a test and the probabilities of Type I and Type II errors

- understand the meaning of 'unbiased' and 'consistent' when applied to estimators and be able to decide between estimators on the basis of their efficiency.

3

Non-parametric tests

Every hypothesis test so far in the course has tested the value of the parameter of a distribution. In each case, either we knew the distribution of the population or the sample size was sufficiently large for the central limit theorem to apply. But in some cases it may be invalid to make assumptions about the nature of the distribution of the population. Or there may be insufficient data for the central limit theorem to apply. Distribution-free or non-parametric tests have been devised which test the *sample median*. This section is concerned with some of these.

By the end of this section you should be able to:

● use the sign test for a single sample and for paired samples

● use the Wilcoxon signed-ranks test in single-sample and matched-pairs examples

● use the Wilcoxon rank sum test in two-sample problems including use of a normal approximation.

The sign test

The following example illustrates the use of the sign test.

Example A keen crossword-puzzle enthusiast calculated ten years ago that his median time for solving *The Times* crossword was 23 minutes. He considers that, either as a result of the crosswords becoming more difficult or perhaps as the result of diminished powers, his median time has increased. To test this hypothesis, he times himself for 10 crosswords and obtains the following data (rounded to the next highest minute):

24   28   29   17   32   18   20   30   26   21

Do the figures provide evidence to support his belief?

Solution As usual we set up two hypotheses as follows:

$$H_0: \text{median} = 23 \quad \text{(i.e. no change)}$$

H$_1$: median > 23   (a one-tailed test since we are testing for a strict increase)

significance level   5%

The first step is to replace each item of data by a + sign or a − sign depending on whether it is above or below the median value assumed in H$_0$, giving

| + | + | + | − | + | − | − | + | + | − |

Now since the population median lies exactly in the middle of the distribution, it follows that the probability that an item of data is above the median $= \frac{1}{2}$ and the probability that an item of data is below the median $= \frac{1}{2}$. So for our list of +'s and −'s, we have a fixed number of independent trials ($n = 10$) and a fixed probability ($p = \frac{1}{2}$) that it is a + or a −.

The distribution of X, the number of + signs is therefore $X \sim B(10, \frac{1}{2})$

The distribution is the same for − signs.

Now for this distribution

$$P(X \geq 10) = \left(\frac{1}{2}\right)^{10} = 0.00098$$

$$P(X \geq 9) = 0.00098 + \binom{10}{9}\left(\frac{1}{2}\right)^{10} = 0.01075$$

$$P(X \geq 8) = 0.01075 + \binom{10}{8}\left(\frac{1}{2}\right)^{10} = 0.0547$$

So while $P(X \geq 8) = 0.05470$

we have $P(X \geq 9) = 0.01075$

The cut-off point for the 5% significance level is taken to be $P(X \geq 9)$ as $P(X \geq 9) < 0.05$ and $P(X \geq 8) > 0.05$.

The critical region (for the rejection of H$_0$) is therefore $X \geq 9$.

Since in the example $X = 6$, we do not reject H$_0$. The man's belief about *The Times* crosswords is not borne out by the evidence.

Several points should be noted about the sign test:

● The test is crude in the sense that the result would have been exactly the same if each of the items of data producing a + had 10 or 20 or any other number of minutes added to them, since we only test for larger or smaller rather than how much larger or smaller.

● Cumulative binomial probability tables can be profitably used as they remove the need to calculate the probabilities each time.

● The normal approximation to B(n,p) can safely be used for quite small values of n as $p = \frac{1}{2}$ in this test.

● If an item of data coincides with the value of the median predicted by the null hypothesis then the value should be rejected and n reduced correspondingly.

The following example illustrates some of these points.

| Example | A group of 7-year-old children was given a standardised reading test and the results, expressed as reading ages, were: |

| | 7.1 | 7.0 | 7.3 | 6.4 | 7.1 | 6.2 | 7.5 | 7.1 |
| | 7.3 | 6.9 | 6.8 | 6.6 |

Is there evidence that this group has a median reading age other than seven years?

| Solution |

H_0: median = 7

H_1: median ≠ 7 (two-tailed test)

5% significance level

Replacing the data by + (> 7) or – (< 7) or ignoring (= 7) gives

+   +   –   +   –   +   +   +   –   –   –

If X is the number of + signs

then $X \sim B(11,\frac{1}{2})$

Now since B(n,$\frac{1}{2}$) is symmetrical we only need to consider one end of the distribution (we need a total probability of up to 0.025 at each end for a 5% critical region):

$$P(X = 0) \quad = \left(\tfrac{1}{2}\right)^{11} \quad = 0.00049$$

$$P(X \le 1) \quad = 0.00049 + \left(\tbinom{11}{1}\right)\left(\tfrac{1}{2}\right)^{11} \quad = 0.00586$$

$$P(X \le 2) \quad = 0.00586 + \left(\tbinom{11}{2}\right)\left(\tfrac{1}{2}\right)^{11} = 0.02686$$

and we reach our cut-off point.

By symmetry, the critical region is $X \le 1$ or $X \ge 10$

since P($X \le 2$) + P($X \ge 9$)   = 0.02686 + 0.02686

= 0.05372

> 0.05

41

whereas $P(X \leq 1) + P(X \geq 10) = 0.00586 + 0.00586$

$$= 0.01172$$

$$< 0.05$$

In the example, $X = 6$, which is well within the acceptance region for H_0. We conclude therefore that there is no reason to suppose that this group of children has a median reading age different from seven years.

Sign test for paired samples

The following example shows how the sign test can be used to decide whether two samples come from populations with the same median.

Example   A fuel-additive manufacturer claims that his new additive will increase the number of miles per gallon (mpg) for the average motorist. Thirteen cars are tested on fuel without the additive and then on the same fuel but with the additive. The following results were obtained:

with additive (mpg)	39.2	33.6	45.8	36.5	41.8	29.6	30.8	47.4	...
without additive (mpg)	38.5	32.7	47.8	36.4	41.2	28.7	31.2	46.5	...

	48.3	38.5	32.9	41.2	46.5
	46.2	38.7	31.6	41.0	46.2

Do the data provide evidence to support the manufacturer's claim?

Solution   In our solution we assume that the only possible difference between the samples is in the value of their respective medians.

To test whether this is the case we look at the signs of the *differences* in their values.

These are:

+   +   −   +   +   +   −   +   +   −   +   +   +

Our null hypothesis is that there is no difference in medians, i.e. the median of differences is zero.

H_0: median of differences $= 0$

H_1: median of differences > 0 (a one-tailed test since we are specifically testing for an increase in mpg)

5% significance level

From here the procedure is the same as with the single-sample test.

If X = number of positive differences then $X \sim B\left(13,\frac{1}{2}\right)$

$$P(X = 13) \;=\; \left(\tfrac{1}{2}\right)^{13} = 0.00012$$

$$P(X \geq 12) \;=\; \left(\tbinom{13}{1}\right)\left(\tfrac{1}{2}\right)^{13} + 0.00012 = 0.00171$$

$$P(X \geq 11) \;=\; \left(\tbinom{13}{2}\right)\left(\tfrac{1}{2}\right)^{13} + 0.00171 = 0.01123$$

$$P(X \geq 10) \;=\; \left(\tbinom{13}{3}\right)\left(\tfrac{1}{2}\right)^{13} + 0.00123 = 0.04614$$

$$P(X \geq 9) \;=\; \left(\tbinom{13}{4}\right)\left(\tfrac{1}{2}\right)^{13} + 0.04614 = 0.13342$$

We have reached a cumulative probability greater than 0.05, so the critical region is $X \geq 10$.

Since our data gives $X = 10$, we are in the critical region for the test and so we reject H_0 in favour of H_1. At the 5% significance level we conclude that there is evidence to support the manufacturer's claim.

Example　Suppose in the previous example that the manufacturer had claimed that performance increased by at least one mpg for the average motorist. How could we test this claim?

Solution　The test is as follows:

Write + for a difference greater than 1, – otherwise, giving

$$-\quad-\quad-\quad-\quad-\quad-\quad-\quad-\quad+\quad-\quad+\quad-\quad-$$

H_0: median of differences ≤ 1

H_1: median of differences > 1

Under H_0 at the limit value of median = 1, the distribution of +'s is $B(13,\frac{1}{2})$

$$P(X \geq 10) \;= 0.04614$$

gives the critical region (as before). Clearly we accept H_0 in this case since $X = 2$.

You should now complete Exercises 1 and 2 on pp. 54–5.

The Wilcoxon signed-ranks test

The statistician Frank Wilcoxon devised tests for population medians which are more sophisticated than the sign test since they take into account the size of the differences from the hypothesised median. The theory behind the tests is beyond 'A' level standard and therefore will not be given here. For the 'A' level examination you need to know when and how to use the test. The following example illustrates the use of the single-sample test in an uncomplicated way.

Example

A person on a 1500 kcal/day diet decides to record his intake for a period of two weeks. The following are his daily recorded values:

1472	1523	1515	1479	1555	1410	1512
1525	1492	1535	1530	1545	1462	1551

Is there evidence at a 5% significance level that his median intake is greater than that prescribed by the diet?

Solution

We make no assumption about the distribution of the values.

The method is as follows:

H_0: median = 1500

H_1: median > 1500   (one-tailed as we are testing for an increase)

5% significance level.

We now consider the difference between the median under H_0 and each item of data giving:

−28	+ 23	+15	−21	+55	−90	+12
+25	−8	+35	+30	+45	−38	+51

Now *ignoring signs*, we rank these differences in increasing size.

Difference	−8	+12	+15	−21	+23	+25	−28	+30	...
Rank	1	2	3	4	5	6	7	8	...

Difference	+35	−38	+45	+51	+55	−90
Rank	9	10	11	12	13	14

Next, we find the sum of the ranks of the positive differences

$$S^+ = 2 + 3 + 5 + 6 + 8 + 9 + 11 + 12 + 13$$
$$= 69$$

and the corresponding sum of the ranks of the negative differences

$$S^- = 1 + 4 + 7 + 10 + 14$$
$$= 36$$

Now under H_0 we would expect these rank-sums to be approximately equal (this assumes the data are evenly spread out on either side of the median).

We now let S equal the smaller of S^+ and S^-. S is the test statistic.

Here $S = 36$.

We turn to the table on p. 233 to find our critical value. For the sample size, go to the row headed 14, and for the significance level, go to the column 0.05. Where these cross we find the value 25. This value is the largest that will lead to rejection of H_0, i.e. any value obtained from the data *less than or equal* to 25 will lead us to reject H_0 in favour of H_1.

In our example we have $S = 36$.

Since $S(\text{calc}) > S(\text{tab})$ we accept H_0 in this case and conclude that at a 5% level of significance there is no evidence to suggest that this person is exceeding the requirements of the diet.

To summarise, the procedure for a Wilcoxon test for a median is:

1   Work out the signed differences from the value of the median given by H_0.

2   Rank these differences, ignoring the signs.

3   Work out S^+, the sum of the ranks of positive differences.

4   Work out S^-, the sum of the ranks of negative differences.

5   Let $S =$ the minimum of S^+ and S^-.

6   Test the value of S by comparing it with the critical value in the table (p. 233).

7   If $S(\text{calc}) > S(\text{tab})$ accept H_0.

The next example goes through this procedure, showing how much working is necessary.

Example   A mathematics exam paper is considered to take an average student 75 minutes to complete. The following times (to the nearest minute) were recorded when the exam paper was tested on a group of 12 students:

73, 68, 83, 74, 86, 62, 79, 81, 80, 84, 72, 89

Test the hypothesis that the median time for this paper is greater than 75 minutes.

Solution H_0: median $= 75$

H_1: median > 75

5% significance level

A table of differences and their associated ranks (ignoring the signs) looks like this:

Difference		−2	−7	+8	−1	+11	−13	+4	+6	...
Rank		2	7	8	1	10	11	4	6	...

Difference		+5	+9	−3	+14
Rank		5	9	3	12

$$S^- = 2 + 7 + 1 + 11 + 3 = 24$$
$$S^+ = 8 + 10 + 4 + 6 + 5 + 9 + 12 = 54$$
$$\Rightarrow \quad S = 24$$

For $n = 12$ at 0.05 significance we find from the tables the value 17.

Since our calculated value of S is greater than 17 we accept H_0. On the evidence of the data given there is no reason to conclude at a 5% level of significance that the median time for the paper is more than 75 minutes.

The Wilcoxon signed-ranks test for matched pairs

Just as the sign test can be adapted to compare the medians of samples, the Wilcoxon test can also be used in this way.

Example   To investigate the effect of alcohol on reaction time, 10 subjects were given a stimulus and their reaction time to that stimulus was recorded. On one occasion the stimulus followed the consumption of alcohol and on another the stimulus was given when alcohol had not previously been consumed. The reaction times, in seconds, were as follows.

Subject	No alcohol	After alcohol
1	5.1	4.7
2	3.1	3.6
3	3.0	2.8
4	3.3	3.0
5	3.6	4.3
6	3.8	4.7
7	5.3	5.9
8	4.9	6.1
9	6.4	6.5
10	1.7	2.5

Stating clearly your hypotheses, carry out

(a)   a sign test

(b)   a Wilcoxon matched-pairs, signed-ranks test

to ascertain whether or not alcohol increases reaction time. In both cases use a 5% level of significance.

Comment on your results.

[ULEAC Specimen paper T3]

Solution   (a)   Sign test:

H_0: alcohol does not increase reaction time

H_1: alcohol increases reaction time (one-tailed)

5% significance level

Differences (After alcohol – No alcohol)

$$- + - - + + + + + +$$

X = number of negative differences

$X \sim B\left(10, \frac{1}{2}\right)$

$P(X = 0) = \left(\frac{1}{2}\right)^{10} = 0.00098$

$P(X \leq 1) = 0.00098 + 0.00977 = 0.01075$

$P(X \leq 2) = 0.01075 + 0.04394 = 0.05470$

giving $X = 1$ as the critical value.

Alternatively,

X = number of positive differences

$X \sim B(10, \frac{1}{2})$

$P(X = 10) = \left(\frac{1}{2}\right)^{10} = 0.00098$

$P(X \geq 9) = 0.00098 + 0.00977 = 0.01075$

$P(X \geq 8) = 0.01075 + 0.04394 = 0.05470$

giving $X = 9$ as the critical value.

Hence H_0 is accepted at the 5% level.

(b)   Wilcoxon test:

H_0: median reaction times are equal

H_1: alcohol increases median reaction time (one-tailed)

5% significance level

Difference	−0.4	+0.5	−0.2	−0.3	+0.7	+0.9	+0.6	+1.2
Rank	4	5	2	3	7	9	6	10

Difference	+0.1	+0.8
Rank	1	8

$$S^+ = 5 + 7 + 9 + 6 + 10 + 1 + 8 = 46$$
$$S^- = 4 + 2 + 3 = 9$$
$$\Rightarrow S = 9$$

From the tables (p. 233) at 5% significance for $n = 10$, we find $S(\text{tab}) = 10$.

Since $S(\text{calc}) < S(\text{tab})$ we are in the critical region for the test and therefore reject H_0 and conclude that the median reaction time has increased.

The Wilcoxon test gives a more reliable result than the sign test as it takes account of the magnitudes of the differences. The subjects who gave a decreased reaction time gave very small differences compared with the subjects who gave an increased reaction time.

Use of a normal approximation for the signed-ranks test

The signed-ranks sum S which is used in the Wilcoxon test above has a distribution which is approximately normal even for quite small values of n. The proof of this is difficult and not required for 'A' level, but its use may be tested. You don't need to remember the result

$$S \sim N\left(\frac{n(n + 1)}{4}, \frac{n(n + 1)(2n + 1)}{24}\right)$$

since it may be found in the *Formula Book*. Since S is a discrete quantity, however, we should apply a continuity correction when finding the value of z (a continuous approximation to it).

Example   A sample of size 18 gave values $S^+ = 20$ and $S^- = 15$ when the null and alternative hypotheses were

H_0: median = 32

H_1: median > 32

Use a normal approximation to test this hypothesis at the 5% level of significance.

Solution	S	$= $ minimum of S^+ and S^-
		$= 15$

$$S \sim N\left(\frac{(18)\,(19)}{4}, \frac{(18)\,(19)\,(37)}{24}\right)$$

$$\sim N(85.5, 527.25)$$

The test statistic, $z = \dfrac{(15 + 0.5) - 85.5}{\sqrt{527.25}} = -3.049$

where we are using the familiar form

$$z = \frac{(S + 0.5) - \mu}{\sigma}$$

The 0.5 added to the value of S is the continuity correction.

Since the critical value for a one-tailed test at the 5% significance level is -1.64, H_0 would be rejected in favour of H_1 in this example.

A two-tailed signed-ranks test

The next example illustrates the use of a Wilcoxon signed-ranks test to determine whether a sample shows a median value different from a given value under H_0 (rather than specifically greater than or less than). The method in this example can easily be adapted to test for a difference between two samples.

Example	Items from a factory production line are packaged in batches. The number of items per packet is nominally 500. A sample of eight packages was tested and gave the following counts:

$$498 \quad 500 \quad 503 \quad 496 \quad 507 \quad 501 \quad 495 \quad 508$$

Use a Wilcoxon signed-ranks test to determine whether the sample supports a median value of 500.

Solution	H_0: median $= 500$
	H_1: median $\neq 500$ (two-tailed test)
	5% significance

Difference	-2	0	3	-4	7	1	-5	8
Rank	3	1	4	5	7	2	6	8

$$S^- = 3 + 5 + 6 = 14$$
$$S^+ = 1 + 4 + 7 + 2 + 8 = 22$$

$$\Rightarrow\ S\ =\ 14$$

Now for a two-tailed test at the 5% significance level we need to take $2\frac{1}{2}\%$ at either end of the distribution. The tables for the Wilcoxon signed-ranks test on p. 233 give critical values at the $2\frac{1}{2}\%$ level.

Reading down the column for sample size to 8 and across to 0.025 we find the value 3. This is the highest value for S which will lead us to reject H_0 (i.e. any value for $S \le 3$ would lead us to reject H_0). In our example, $S = 14$, and so we are well within the acceptance region for H_0. On the evidence of the sample, we don't need to reject the value of 500 as the median.

The Wilcoxon rank-sum test

The Wilcoxon rank-sum test is used in situations where it is necessary to test whether two samples, which may not be equal in size, are random samples from the same population. The example that follows shows in detail how to conduct such a test.

Example

Eleven children in a primary school class were given a geometric task to perform to test their spatial awareness. The times for the boys to complete the task were:

142 136 121 154 155 128 seconds

and the times for the girls to complete the task were:

133 126 124 132 141 seconds

Do these times come from the same population? Or does the sample show that there is a significant difference between boys' and girls' spatial awareness?

Solution

Rank the sample values together as if they were from a single sample (in ascending order):

Combined data	121	124	126	128	132	133	136	141	142
Rank	1	2	3	4	5	6	7	8	9

Combined data	154	155
Rank	10	11

The ranks of the data values from the *smaller* sample have been underlined.

The test statistic is the sum of these underlined ranks:

$$T\ =\ 2 + 3 + 5 + 6 + 8$$
$$=\ 24$$

Now, if we are claiming that the sets of data come from the same population, then values from the combined sample should be fairly evenly spread about the common median value. The smaller the value of T the more uneven this spread will be and the more we will be inclined to reject the hypothesis that the samples come from the same population.

Formally, H_0: the two sets of data have a common median.

H_1: the median of the second sample $\neq$ median of the first sample (two-tailed test)

5% significance

We have calculated the test statistic $T = 24$. We now compare this value with the value given in the tables for the Wilcoxon rank-sum test (p. 232).

Since we are conducting a 5% two-tailed test we are looking at $2\frac{1}{2}\%$ of the distribution at either end. We need, therefore, to use the top half of the table:

n_1 is the size of the smaller sample = 5

n_2 is the size of the larger sample = 6

Reading along for n_1 and down for n_2 we find a value of 18.

This is the critical value for the test, and a value of $T \leq 18$ will lead us to reject H_0 in favour of H_1. (This is comparable with the way in which we used the tables for the signed-rank test.)

Since $T(\text{calc}) > T(\text{tab})$ we accept H_0 in this example at the 5% level.

The data clearly exhibit a tendency towards lower times for girls, but the test has shown that this is not by a *statistically significant* amount. The next example shows a solution more concisely.

Example	

Example

The number of phone calls per hour to a busy office was recorded on a Monday when office hours are 9 am – 5 pm and on a Friday when office hours are 9 am – 4 pm. The figures are shown below.

Mon	28	38	43	47	42	40	32	21
Fri	22	31	45	36	27	29	14	

Test whether there is any difference between the frequency of calls for these days.

Solution

Combined data	14	21	22	27	28	29	31	32	36
Rank	1	2	3	4	5	6	7	8	9

Combined data	38	40	42	43	45	47
Rank	10	11	12	13	14	15

Underlined ranks are from the second (smaller) sample.

H_0: there is no difference in the frequency of calls on Mondays and Fridays

H_1: the frequency of calls on Mondays is different from the frequency on Fridays

5% significance

$$T = 1 + 3 + 4 + 6 + 7 + 9 + 14$$
$$= 44$$

Since this is a two-tailed test we need to refer to the top half of the table. $n_1 = 7$, $n_2 = 8$ and the 0.025 level gives the value 38.

Since $T(\text{calc}) > T(\text{tab})$ we accept H_0. According to these samples, there is no detectable difference in the frequency of calls on Mondays and Fridays.

The following example illustrates a one-tailed test.

Example

A sample A of size 17 and a sample B of size 16 were ranked a single sample and gave a value $T = 186$.

Test whether the median of sample A is greater than the median of sample B at the 5% level of significance.

Solution

We have $n_1 = 16$

$n_2 = 17$

H_0: median of sample A = median of sample B

H_1: median of sample A > median of sample B (one-tailed test)

$T = 186$

Using the lower table on p. 232 we find a critical value of 225. Since $T(\text{calc}) < T(\text{tab})$ we reject H_0.

Using the normal approximation for a rank-sum test

The tables for the Wilcoxon rank-sum test are suitable for examples in which the size of the smaller sample is ≤ 20. For samples of equal size, the lower sum of ranks should be used in the test.

In this case, add up the ranks for each sample (after ranking as if it were a single sample) and select the lower of the two for comparison with the value in the tables. In examples where the smaller sample is of size > 20 then we can use the fact that the statistic T has an approximately normal distribution with parameters shown in the following expression.

$$T \sim N\left(\frac{n_1(n_1 + n_2 + 1)}{2}, \frac{n_1 n_2(n_1 + n_2 + 1)}{12}\right)$$

where n_1 = the sample size of the smaller sample

n_2 = the sample size of the larger sample.

You don't need to memorise this expression as it appears in the *Formula Book*. You will need to know the meaning of n_1 and n_2 (n_1 is the size of the *smaller* sample).

In the case where the samples are of equal size we would decide which is n_1 and n_2 after the ranking. If the first sample gave a smaller rank-sum then its size would be n_1 in the above expression.

Example

Two brands of baked beans were tested for sugar content. Brand 1 is a more expensive variety and Brand 2 is a cheaper supermarket 'own-brand' alternative. The results are shown in the table (g/100 g):

Brand 1	1.83	1.92	2.14	2.20	1.98	1.87	1.72	1.97
Brand 2	1.76	2.84	2.19	1.82	2.04	2.28	1.86	

Is there evidence that Brand 2 contains more sugar?

Solution

H_0: sugar concentrations are the same for Brand 1 and Brand 2.

H_1: sugar concentration is higher for Brand 2 than for Brand 1 (one-tailed test).

Significance level 5%

Combined data	1.72	1.76	1.82	1.83	1.86	1.87	1.92	1.97	1.98
Rank	1	2	3	4	5	6	7	8	9

Combined data	2.04	2.19	2.20	2.14	2.28	2.84
Rank	10	11	12	13	14	15

$$T = 2 + 3 + 5 + 10 + 11 + 14 + 15$$
$$= 60$$

$$T \sim N\left(\frac{(7)\,(16)}{2}, \frac{(7)\,(8)\,(16)}{12}\right)$$

$$\sim N(56, 8.641^2)$$

Using a continuity correction

$$z = \frac{60.5 - 56}{8.641} = 0.5208$$

since $0.5208 < 1.645$ (the critical value from normal-distribution tables).

The null hypothesis is accepted, i.e. there is no significant difference in sugar content.

This example is used for illustrating the use of the normal approximation only, and the test here could have been carried out using tables.

You should now be able to complete the exercises at the end of this section.

EXERCISES

1 The following data are thought to come from a population having median = 25. Conduct a sign test at the 5% level of significance to test this claim.

28.2   21.5   24.6   25.3   29.1   27.4   26.2   24.8   25.0   28.7   31.4   28.1

2 A university department is deciding which of two research proposals to support. It asked 11 members of staff to read the proposals and to award each of them a mark out of 100. The marks awarded were as follows:

Member of staff	1	2	3	4	5	6	7	8	9	10	11
Proposal 1	89	37	70	21	29	36	11	46	74	47	26
Proposal 2	95	49	69	86	30	99	19	52	30	45	80

Use the sign test at the 5% significance level to test whether proposal 2 is better than proposal 1.

[AEB 1994]

3 Test the data from Question 1 using Wilcoxon's signed-rank test.

4 The following table gives the results (%) in Physics and Maths tests for a group of students. Use a Wilcoxon test at the 5% significance level to determine whether there is any significant difference in the median scores:

Maths mark	38	59	47	63	58	85	41	82	73	65
Physics mark	27	58	53	73	62	63	39	89	65	70

5 Use a normal approximation to S to test the data in Question 4 (5% significance).

6 Some Year 11 students were asked to assess the time spent on homework in a given week. Ten females and nine males completed the task and reported the following times (minutes):

Males	350	200	240	0	210	285	420	180	60	
Females	280	120	520	190	320	220	290	90	150	300

Use the data to test the hypothesis that there is no difference between male and female students with respect to the time spent on homework. Test at the 5% level of significance.

7 A random sample of five children from Class *A* was selected and each child was given the same puzzle to solve. The number of minutes to the nearest minute taken by each child to solve the puzzle was recorded and the results are shown below.

Class *A*: 13, 16, 8, 10, 11

Similarly a random sample of six children was taken from Class *B* and their times to solve the puzzle are recorded below.

Class *B*: 12, 22, 18, 17, 15, 20.

(a) Give a reason to justify using the Wilcoxon rank sum test to test whether or not there is any difference between the median times taken by the children.

(b) Stating clearly your hypotheses, carry out this test using a 5% level of significance.

Eventually all the children in both classes were given the puzzle to solve. There were 25 children in each class and the T value obtained for Class A was 522.

(c) Again using the Wilcoxon rank sum test and a 5% level of significance, test whether there is any difference between the classes in terms of the median times taken to solve this puzzle.

[ULEAC 1966]

SUMMARY   At the end of this section you should be able to:

- use the sign test for a single-sample median
- use the sign test to test the difference between the medians of paired samples
- understand how and when to use the Wilcoxon signed-ranks test for a single sample and a matched-pairs sample
- use the normal approximation to S
- conduct Wilcoxon ranked-sum tests in two-sample problems
- use the normal approximation to T.

4

Regression

This section continues the work of *Statistics 2*, Section 6.

By the end of the section you should be able to:

- calculate and use residuals
- calculate and use the residual sum of squares
- test hypotheses about β, the gradient of the line of best fit
- calculate confidence intervals for β.

The linear regression model

Throughout this section we will assume that y is the response (or dependent) variable and that x is the explanatory (or independent) variable and that the data consist of pairs (x_i, y_i) where $1 \le i \le n, i \in \mathbb{Z}$

Often an experimenter will decide on particular values for one variable (x) which then determine values for the other variable (y). Evidence from scatter graphs and calculation of the correlation coefficient may suggest that a linear relationship exists between x and y (or perhaps between simple functions of these such as y and $\frac{1}{x}$ or $\log y$ and x) but that the points do not lie exactly on a straight line because of hidden random effects. (There may be effects outside the experimenter's control or perhaps the result of experimental errors, such as errors of measurement.)

This situation is expressed in the formula

$$y_i = \alpha + \beta x_i + \varepsilon_i \qquad \text{(where } \varepsilon_i \sim N(0, \sigma^2))$$

where the ε_i are (unknown) error terms and, as usual, α and β are the intercept and gradient of the line of best fit.

The error terms ε_i are assumed to come from independent normal distributions with mean zero and variance σ^2. (This is a reasonable assumption to make since there is no reason to suppose that random effects or experimental errors should be biased asymmetrically about zero.)

As outlined in *Statistics 2*, a line of best fit can be calculated from the value

$$R = \sum_{i=1}^{n} (y_i - \alpha - \beta x_i)^2$$

By calculus methods outside the 'A' level syllabus, the value of R is minimised and estimators of α and β are obtained.

These are calculated from the formulae

$$\hat{\beta} = \frac{S_{xy}}{S_{xx}} = \frac{\sum_{i=1}^{n} (x_i y_i) - n\bar{x}\,\bar{y}}{\sum_{i=1}^{n} (x_i^2) - n\bar{x}^2}$$

$$\hat{\alpha} = \bar{y} - \hat{\beta}\,\bar{x}.$$

$\hat{\beta}$ is called the least-squares estimator of β (the gradient) and $\hat{\alpha}$ is called the least-squares estimator of α (the intercept) of the line of best fit.

Residuals

Once the line of best fit has been obtained by the methods summarised above (so that values of $\hat{\alpha}$ and $\hat{\beta}$ have been calculated using all of the values of x_i and y_i), we can check that the particular linear model obtained is appropriate. There are several ways of doing this. We can do a visual check by simply plotting the points (x_i, y_i) and the line $y = \hat{\alpha} + \hat{\beta}x$. This can show up any rogue points, or *outliers* as they are called. A graph showing outliers is given in Figure 4.1.

Figure 4.1

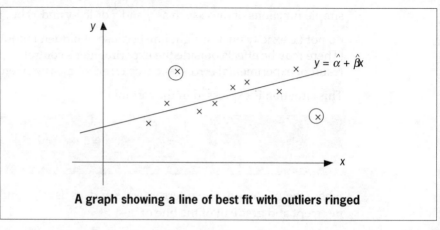

A graph showing a line of best fit with outliers ringed

A more precise numerical method of detecting outliers is to examine the values of the error terms given by

$$\varepsilon_i = y_i - (\hat{\alpha} + \hat{\beta}x_i)$$

The calculation of the difference between the actual values of the dependent variable and the values predicted for them by the proposed linear model is called *residual analysis*, and the values obtained are called *residuals*. As an example, consider the following:

Example

For the data shown in the table, the model $y = a + bx$ is to be considered. Find the equation of the regression line in this form (i.e. regression of y on x) and calculate the residuals.

x_i	1.3	1.5	1.7	1.9	2.1	2.3	2.5	2.7	2.9	3.1	3.3
y_i	6.9	7.4	8.0	8.5	11.1	9.4	9.8	10.2	10.8	11.4	11.7

Solution

The data are summarised as follows:

$$n = 11, \quad \Sigma x_i = 25.3, \quad \Sigma y_i = 105.2, \quad \Sigma x_i^2 = 62.59, \quad \Sigma x_i y_i = 252.06$$

giving $\bar{x} = 2.3$, $\bar{y} = 9.5636$ (4 d.p.)

$$\hat{\beta} = \frac{252.06 - (11)(2.3)(9.5636)}{62.59 - (11)(2.3)^2}$$

$$= 2.2957 \quad \text{(4 d.p.)}$$

$$\hat{\alpha} = 9.5636 - (2.2957)(2.3)$$

$$= 4.284 \quad \text{(3 d.p.)}$$

giving the line of best fit

$$y = 4.284 + 2.295x \quad \text{(3 d.p.)}$$

The table of residuals is now calculated as

x_i	y_i	$\hat{\alpha} + \hat{\beta}x_i$	ε_i
1.3	6.9	7.2679	−0.368
1.5	7.4	7.7271	−0.327
1.7	8.0	8.1862	−0.186
1.9	8.5	8.6453	−0.145
2.1	11.1	9.1045	1.996
2.3	9.4	9.5636	−0.164
2.5	9.8	10.0228	−0.223
2.7	10.2	10.4819	−0.282
2.9	10.8	10.9410	−0.141
3.1	11.4	11.4002	0.000
3.3	11.7	11.8593	−0.159
			0.001

Note that $\sum_{i=1}^{n} \varepsilon_i \approx 0$ and that the table clearly shows that the fifth observation may well be an outlier; it is by far the largest value. Perhaps this observation was a result of an error in a measuring instrument or a careless moment on the part of the experimenter. Its inclusion in the calculation for $\hat{\alpha}$ and $\hat{\beta}$ will distort these values away from those suggested by the small values for ε_i the other pairs (x_i, y_i) give. We might therefore re-calculate $\hat{\alpha}$ and $\hat{\beta}$ without this pair and examine the new residuals.

Example   For the data in the previous exercise, find new values for $\hat{\alpha}$ and $\hat{\beta}$, omitting the pair (2.1, 11.1) and calculate the new residuals.

Solution   For the modified data we have:

$$n = 10, \quad \Sigma x_i = 23.2, \quad \Sigma y_i = 94.1, \quad \Sigma x_i^2 = 58.18, \quad \Sigma x_i y_i = 228.75$$

giving $\bar{x} = 2.32, \ \bar{y} = 9.41$

$$\hat{\beta} = \frac{228.75 - (10)\,(2.32)\,(9.41)}{58.18 - (10)\,(2.32)^2}$$

$$= 2.396 \qquad (3 \text{ d.p.})$$

$$\hat{\alpha} = 9.41 - (2.396)\,(2.32)$$

$$= 3.851 \qquad (3 \text{ d.p.})$$

The new line of best fit is therefore

$$y = 3.851 + 2.396x \quad \text{(3 d.p.).}$$

The new table of residuals is:

x_i	y_i	$\hat{\alpha} + \hat{\beta}x_i$	ε_i
1.3	6.9	6.9658	−0.066
1.5	7.4	7.4450	−0.045
1.7	8.0	7.9242	0.076
1.9	8.5	8.4035	0.096
2.3	9.4	9.3620	0.038
2.5	9.8	9.8412	−0.041
2.7	10.2	10.3204	−0.121
2.9	10.8	10.7997	0.000
3.1	11.4	11.2789	0.121
3.3	11.7	11.7582	−0.058
			0.082

This model seems more likely, and we might justifiably conclude that the pair (2.1, 11.1) was an isolated outlier and should be excluded from the calculations. In some experimental circumstances, it may be possible to make a new observation of y when x takes the value 2.1.

In principle, we could repeat the exercise with our refined model, perhaps considering that $x = 2.7$ and $x = 3.1$ also give slightly high values for ε_i compared with the other observations. In practice, the process has to stop somewhere – otherwise we might reduce our set of data to a single observation, which would clearly be absurd. We have to decide, before conducting the experiment, on the kind of ε-value which would be considered too extreme to include in the final model.

However, this method illustrates an important aspect of mathematical modelling; namely that we can start with a fairly crude model and, in the light of evidence, refine it to produce a more exact one. Residual analysis provides a good illustration of this process.

The residual sum of squares

You have already seen that in the hypothetical linear model the errors ε_i come from a normal distribution, namely

$$\varepsilon_i \sim N(0,\sigma^2)$$

We can estimate the value of σ^2 in the distribution using the *residual sum of squares* (RSS) which is calculated from

$$RSS = \sum_{i=1}^{n} \varepsilon_i^2$$

where the ε_i are the residuals we calculated in the previous section.

Now, since $y_i = \hat{\alpha} + \hat{\beta}x_i + \varepsilon_i$

we have $\varepsilon_i = y_i - \hat{\alpha} - \hat{\beta}x_i$

$$\Rightarrow \quad \varepsilon_i^2 = (y_i - \hat{\alpha} - \hat{\beta}x_i)^2$$

$$\Rightarrow \quad \sum \varepsilon_i^2 = \sum(y_i - \hat{\alpha} - \hat{\beta}x_i)^2$$

which after some complicated algebraic manipulation reduces to

$$\sum \varepsilon_i^2 = S_{yy} - \frac{(S_{xy})^2}{S_{xx}}$$

We can reduce it even further to

$$\sum \varepsilon_i^2 = S_{yy}(1 - r^2)$$

where r is the value of the product moment correlation coefficient. A later example will confirm the equality of these expressions.

An estimate of the variance of the distribution of the error terms is calculated from the formula

$$s^2 = \frac{RSS}{n-2} = \frac{\sum_{i=1}^{n} \varepsilon_i^2}{n-2}$$

The following example illustrates the various calculations involved.

Example

For the following data, the model $y_i = \alpha + \beta x_i + \varepsilon_i$ is considered appropriate where $\varepsilon_i \sim N(0, \sigma^2)$:

x_i	10	12	14	16	18	20	22	24	26	28	30
y_i	−1.62	−2.29	−3.01	−3.92	−4.21	−4.79	−5.49	−6.13	−6.73	−7.41	−8.01

Calculate the least squares estimates of α and β, the values of the residuals and of the RSS. Use the value of the RSS to find an estimate of σ^2 and confirm that $RSS = S_{yy} - \dfrac{(S_{xy})^2}{S_{xx}}$.

Comment on the appropriateness of the model and suggest any modifications that could be made to improve it.

<table>
<tr><td>**Solution**</td><td>The summary calculations for the data give</td></tr>
</table>

$$n = 11, \quad \Sigma x_i = 220, \quad \Sigma y_i = -53.61, \quad \Sigma x_i^2 = 4840, \quad \Sigma y_i^2 = 305.0413$$

$$\Sigma x_i y_i = -1210.78$$

leading to

$$S_{xx} = 4840 - \frac{220^2}{11} = 440$$

$$S_{yy} = 305.0413 - \frac{(-53.61)^2}{11} = 43.7657$$

$$S_{xy} = -1210.78 - \frac{(220)(-53.61)}{11} = -138.58$$

$$\hat{\beta} = \frac{-138.58}{440} = -0.3150$$

$$\hat{\alpha} = \frac{-53.61}{11} - \left(\frac{220}{11}\right)(-0.3150)$$

$$= 1.4255$$

A table showing ε_i and ε_i^2 looks like this:

x_i	y_i	$\hat{\alpha} + \hat{\beta}x_i$	ε_i	ε_i^2
10	−1.62	−1.724	0.104	0.012
12	−2.29	−2.354	0.064	0.004
14	−3.01	−2.984	−0.026	0.001
16	−3.92	−3.614	−0.306	0.094
18	−4.21	−4.244	0.034	0.001
20	−4.79	−4.874	0.084	0.007
22	−5.49	−5.504	0.014	0.000
24	−6.13	−6.134	0.004	0.000
26	−6.73	−6.764	0.034	0.001
28	−7.41	−7.394	−0.016	0.000
30	−8.01	−8.024	0.014	0.000
			−0.004	0.12

Calculating $S_{yy} - \dfrac{(S_{xy})^2}{S_{xx}}$

gives RSS $= 43.7657 - \dfrac{(-138.58)^2}{440}$

$= 0.1193$ as required.

(The small difference is a result of rounding.)

The estimate of σ^2 is given by

$$s^2 \;=\; \frac{0.12}{9} \;=\; 0.013$$

giving $s \approx 0.115$.

Comments

The value $\Sigma \varepsilon_i \approx 0$ is a good check on the accuracy of the calculations.

The values of ε_i are all fairly small, only one of them, for the point $(16, -3.92)$, lying outside one standard deviation of the mean of zero.

This means each ε_i has the property

$$|\,\varepsilon_i\,| < s$$

apart from that at $x = 16$.

We may therefore consider modifying the model by ignoring the pair $(16, -3.92)$ or perhaps recalculating or re-reading this value. This is set as an exercise at the end of this section.

You should now be able to complete Exercises 1 and 2 at the end of the section.

Hypothesis test for β

As with any other statistic used to estimate a parameter, we can test whether the value of β (estimated from the data by the value of $\hat{\beta}$) is significantly different from zero or from some other assigned value. The nature of the test statistic and its distribution will depend on whether we know the variance in the distribution of $\varepsilon_i \sim N(0,\sigma^2)$. In circumstances where σ^2 is known, we use a normal distribution, but where $s^2 = \dfrac{\text{RSS}}{n-2}$ is used as an estimate of σ^2 we need to use the t-distribution. In practice, we are unlikely to know the value of σ^2 so we usually need to use the t-distribution.

The sampling distribution of $\hat{\beta}$ is

$$\hat{\beta} \sim N\left(\beta, \frac{\sigma^2}{S_{xx}}\right)$$

Where s^2 is used to estimate σ^2 we use the t-distribution with $n - 2$ degrees of freedom. This is best seen from examples.

Example

Calculation on 12 pairs of values (x_i, y_i) gives the following values:

$$S_{xy} = 72.2$$
$$S_{yy} = 74.6$$
$$S_{xx} = 64.5$$

It is known that $\varepsilon_i \sim N(0, 0.6^2)$.

Test the hypothesis that $\beta = 1$ at the 5% level of significance.

Solution

$H_0: \beta = 1$

$H_1: \beta \neq 1$

5% significance

$$\hat{\beta} = \frac{S_{xy}}{S_{xx}} = \frac{72.2}{64.5} = 1.1194$$

The test statistic is

$$\frac{\hat{\beta}}{\sigma/\sqrt{S_{xx}}} = \frac{1.1194 - 1}{0.6/\sqrt{64.5}} = 1.5982$$

Since $1.5982 < 1.96$, we would accept the null hypothesis in this case.

The next example illustrates the case when σ^2 is not known but an estimate is used instead.

Example

It is thought that the variables x and y have the following linear relationship:

$$y = 4x + 2 + \varepsilon_i$$
$$\text{where } \varepsilon_i \sim N(0, \sigma^2)$$

The following summary statistics are obtained:

$$n = 15$$
$$S_{xy} = 322.8$$
$$S_{yy} = 1230.6$$
$$S_{xx} = 86.6$$

Test the hypothesis that $\beta = 4$ against the hypothesis that $\beta < 4$ at the 5% significance level.

$H_0: \beta = 4$

$H_1: \beta < 4$

5% significance

$$\hat{\beta} = \frac{322.8}{86.6} = 3.7275$$

$$RSS = 1230.6 - \frac{322.8^2}{86.6}$$

$$= 27.3686$$

Estimated value of σ^2 is $\dfrac{RSS}{n-2}$ giving

$$s^2 = \frac{27.3686}{13}$$

$$\Rightarrow s = 1.4510 \quad (4 \text{ d.p.})$$

The test statistic is

$$\frac{\hat{\beta} - \beta}{s/\sqrt{S_{xx}}} = \frac{3.7275 - 4}{(1.4510/\sqrt{86.6})} = -1.7477 \quad (4 \text{ d.p.})$$

Since we have used s as an estimator of σ, this statistic is distributed t_{n-2} in general and so t_{13} in this example.

The critical value from the tables (p. 234) is –1.771, and since –1.7477 > –1.771 we are just within the acceptance region for H_0.

Confidence intervals for β

The same principles and methods apply to confidence intervals for β as for the earlier statistics. When the value of σ is known we use the fact that

$$\frac{\hat{\beta} - \beta}{\sigma/\sqrt{S_{xx}}} \sim N(0,1)$$

When, as is more likely, the value of σ is estimated from s, we use the fact that

$$\frac{\hat{\beta} - \beta}{s/\sqrt{S_{xx}}} \sim t_{n-2}$$

where s is calculated from $\dfrac{RSS}{n-2}$.

For the summarised data in the example on p. 65, find a 95% confidence interval for β.

Solution

Using the fact that $\dfrac{\hat{\beta} - \beta}{\sigma/\sqrt{S_{xx}}} \sim N(0,1)$

we have the confidence interval

$$1.1194 \pm (1.96) \left(\dfrac{0.6}{\sqrt{64.5}} \right)$$

giving the interval

$$1.1194 \pm 0.1464$$

i.e. $(0.97, 1.27)$ (2 d.p.)

Example

For the summarised data in the example on page 66, find a 95% confidence interval for β.

Solution

Using the result that $\dfrac{\hat{\beta} - \beta}{s/\sqrt{S_{xx}}} \sim t_{13}$

the interval will be

$$3.7275 \pm (2.160) \left(\dfrac{1.4510}{\sqrt{86.6}} \right)$$

giving 3.7275 ± 0.3368

i.e. $(3.39, 4.06)$ (2 d.p.)

You should now be able to complete the exercises below.

EXERCISES

1 For the data in the example on p. 62, recalculate $\hat{\alpha}$, $\hat{\beta}$, $\Sigma \varepsilon_i$, $\Sigma \varepsilon_i^2$, RSS and s^2 but without the pair $(16, -3.92)$. Confirm that this provides a better model for the data and comment on the values of the new ε_i compared with the new s.

2 A chemist measured the speed, y, of an enzymatic reaction at 12 different concentrations, x, of the substrate and eleven of the results are given below:

x	$\frac{1}{2}$	$\frac{1}{3}$	$\frac{1}{4}$	$\frac{1}{6}$	$\frac{1}{7}$	$\frac{1}{8}$	$\frac{1}{9}$	$\frac{1}{10}$	$\frac{1}{11}$	$\frac{1}{12}$	$\frac{1}{13}$
y	0.204	0.218	0.189	0.172	0.142	0.149	0.111	0.125	0.123	0.112	0.096

The chemist thought that the model relating y and x could be of the form

$$y = a + \frac{b}{x}$$

(a) Plot a scatter diagram of y against $\frac{1}{x}$.

(b) Find the equation of the regression line in the above form, giving the coefficients to three significant figures.

(You may use $\Sigma \left(\frac{1}{x}\right)^2 = 793$ and $\Sigma \left(\frac{y}{x}\right) = 11.23$.)

(c) Find, to two significant figures, the sum of squares of residuals for your equation. (You may use $S_{yy} = 0.01684$.)

Originally the data included an observation $(\frac{1}{5}, 0.090)$, and the initial model used by the chemist was a linear regression model for y on $\frac{1}{x}$, for all observations.

(d) Plot this point on your scatter diagram and explain why you think this value has been omitted.

The sum of squares of the residuals of the equation which included the observation $(\frac{1}{5}, 0.090)$ is 0.0082.

(e) Compare this residual sum of squares with the value calculated in (c) and comment whether the difference is consistent with your answer to (d).

(f) What conclusion would you draw about the validity of the chemist's model? State a more refined model you would regard as more reasonable.

[ULEAC Specimen paper T3]

3 (a) The owner of an ice-cream stand believes that there is a linear relationship between the temperature x, in degrees fahrenheit, and the number of ice-creams sold, y. Data are collected between 12.00 noon and 1.00 pm on 20 weekdays. The average number of ice-creams sold during this hour was 35.6 and the average temperature at 12.30 pm over the 20 days was 87.4°.

The following statistics were calculated:

$$S_{xy} = 8.4, \quad S_{xx} = 28.1, \quad S_{yy} = 3.9$$

(i) Find the equation of the least squares regression line in the form $y = a + bx$.

(ii) Test that the regression coefficient is greater than zero. Use a 5% level of significance.

(b) A regression line was fitted to a set of 21 observations. The residual sum of squares was 83.10 and the residuals were as shown below.

1.1	−0.8	2.6	1.5	0.2	−0.4	0.8
−1.8	−2.3	0.9	−2.7	3.1	−1.0	−1.3
4.5	−3.4	−0.1	−0.2	2.4	−1.7	−1.4

It is suggested that for residuals, 95% of them should lie within two standard deviations of the mean.

Comment on this statement in relation to the above residuals.

[ULEAC 1996]

4 For the modified data in Exercise 1, test the hypothesis that $\beta = -0.3$ against the alternative hypothesis $\beta \neq -0.3$ at a 5% significance level.

5 For the modified data in Exercise 1, find a 98% confidence interval for the value of β.

SUMMARY

By the end of this section you should be able to:

- use residuals to locate outliers and improve a linear model where appropriate
- use the RSS to find an estimate for σ^2
- use a normal distribution or a t-distribution to test a hypothesis about β
- use a normal distribution or a t-distribution to find a confidence interval for β.

5

Experimental design

Before we carry out an investigation and collect our data, we need to plan our approach quite carefully. There are a number of factors which have to be considered. If we don't include them in our planning we run the risk of ending up with a meaningless set of figures. In this section we shall be looking at ways of designing experiments which allow for these factors and so increase the chance of a meaningful result.

At the end of this section you should be able to:

- identify the factors and response variables involved in an experimental situation

- understand the basic principles of experimental design and how they are applied in practice

- divide up the experimental population in a suitable way

- use blocking and randomised block design to assign values or levels

- know how to use a Latin square design when three factors may affect the outcome of an experiment.

Origins

The basic ideas of experimental design come from early attempts to make investigations in agriculture more scientific. Farmers wanted to know which variety of crop gave the best yield, for example.

Problems arose because the yield is affected by several factors, not just the variety. Drainage, quantity and quality of fertiliser, water, fertility of the land can all make a substantial difference to the final result. If we plant two varieties of potato, A and B, and the yield from A is bigger, does that mean that variety A will generally produce a bigger yield or was it because the land on which it was planted was better? A method for sorting out which effect belonged to which factor was needed. This led to the idea of experimental design and corresponding ways of analysing the data that we have today.

Before we look more closely at the principles of experimental design, we ought to be clear about some of the terms that are commonly used in this context.

Factors/Levels

Anything which produces an effect on the quantity we're interested in is called a *factor*. So if we are interested in the yield of a plant, possible factors might be the amount of light, water, fertiliser, quality of soil and so on. Before we start an experiment, we should have a fair idea of the factors which might have an effect and include them in our design. If we are unable for some reason to keep them constant, we might include different *levels* of the factor. For instance, if we need to use four different people as operators in a test on cars, we would have four levels of this factor, say I: Matilda, II: Jack, III: Laura and IV: Liam.

If time of day might be a factor, and we can't carry out experiments simultaneously, we would need to include this in our design. The different levels of this factor might be I: 10–12 am, II: 12–2 pm, III: 2–4 pm and IV: 4–6 pm.

Experiment

There's a difference between carrying out a definite experiment and making some observations. In an *experiment* we try to keep as many of the conditions as possible the same throughout, ideally varying just one factor so that the corresponding effects can be measured. In this way, we are able to say that the effect was caused by the particular level of the factor. If we simply make observations we may be able to establish some correlation between two factors, like: the shorter the days get, the more people there are in town on a Saturday. This doesn't necessarily mean that there are more people in town because the nights are longer: some other factor could be operating, like the fact that Christmas is coming.

Response variable

This is the variable that is measured in order to assess the effect of the factors.

A typical example of a *response variable* in an agricultural experiment would be the yield of the crop, which could be measured in kilograms, against different levels of one or more factors. In any experiment, the response variable needs to be well defined and measurable in the least subjective way possible. The yield in kilograms of a crop of tomatoes can be measured quite easily. If we are interested in the taste of the tomatoes, the response variable is much more subjective, and we might need to adopt a different approach. So when planning an experiment – possibly for your project, if you are going on to take T4 – make sure that you will be able to collect and measure your results easily. Quantities such as response time, number of mistakes, wear on tyres, miles per gallon etc. would all be suitable response variables.

These are some of the elements which you will find mentioned in any discussion of experimental design. We'll look now at the principles behind the design schemes, the problems involved and the methods that have evolved in an attempt to overcome them.

Basic principles

Generally speaking, when we carry out an experiment, we are interested in comparing two (or more) means. The average yield of variety A against the average yield of variety B, the average time taken by student C against the average time taken by student D, and so on. It's not enough, however, to compare two figures: we need also to put the figures into some kind of context.

Suppose, for example, that we took a sample of wheat given fertiliser A and another given fertiliser B. The mean yield for A was 20 and for B was 22. Does this mean that the fertilisers produce different yields? The answer is that it depends on the spread, or variance. If the samples look like this

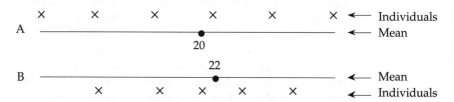

the difference is probably not significant: it could be accounted for by chance. On the other hand, if the samples look like this

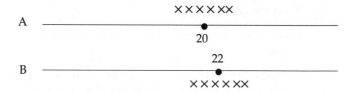

the difference is probably significant because the samples are less widely spread.

So we are interested in two separate population parameters, the mean and the variance, and we need both to compare the two test results. We need, besides an estimate for the mean, to be able to form an estimate of the underlying variance. To do this, we need to keep all the factors constant and run a series of identical experiments. This process is called *replication*. From the results that these give, we can find an unbiased estimate of the variance.

This sounds like a reasonably straightforward procedure. Things, however, are not quite so simple.

Problems

The trouble comes because when we start collecting information, we collect more than we had bargained for. We then have to sort out which parts of the information are useful and which parts can be disregarded. Suppose, for example, that Tilly wanted to know which dress she should wear to a university interview. She asks her friend Vrinda, who tells her that she would look best in the black one. But Tilly knows from past experience of her friend that Vrinda not only likes black clothes in general, but also is very polite. She might have said the black one because she knew that it was Tilly's favourite and wanted to be told to wear it. This is an example of personal bias on the part of the subject, Vrinda, and of the experimenter, Tilly, making it difficult to reach an objective assessment.

We can have the same problem in an experiment of a more scientific nature. Basically, it arises because we cannot reproduce the conditions exactly for each experiment. If we're planting a crop, we cannot guarantee that the seeds are exactly the same, or the soil that they're planted in is equally fertile. If people have volunteered to help with an experiment, we may find that they are not all equally skilled or experienced. When we try to find an estimate for the variance of the factor we're interested in, it could be that the estimate will include variation from factors that we are possibly unaware of. The effect of this will be to increase the size of our estimate for the variance to such an extent that it masks any variation from a possible real difference, in the factor(s) that we are testing.

This was a brief discussion of the problems faced by anybody carrying out an experiment. In summary, they are:

● bias on the part of the subject

● bias on the part of the experimenter

● extra factors (possibly unknown) having an effect on the response variable.

Pairing

We have already said that we need to keep conditions as constant as possible so that we can form some idea of the naturally occurring variation present in the variable we're interested in. Ideally, if there is only one factor, we try and form pairs: one half of each pair is treated and the other not, or one half of each pair has treatment A and the other treatment B. So if we are comparing car tyres, the most sensitive test might be to fit one wheel with one make of tyre and the other wheel on the same axle with the other make. If we are comparing dog food, we might take as our subjects two dogs from the same litter, as alike in character as possible. If we are testing a drug, we might form two groups by finding a set of pairs of similar people and put one of each pair into each group. In this way, the groups as a whole will be as closely matched as possible. This procedure cuts down the effects of untested factors.

Randomisation

In the previous section we mentioned an experiment to test drugs. In such experiments, where there is a possibly large subjective element present, we try and remove any tendency towards bias by forming the groups as outlined above. Once we have a sufficient number to ensure a statistically significant result, we assign the members of the pairs *at random* to form the two groups. This can be done by tossing a coin or using random numbers. Then one of the groups, which can also be chosen at random, is given the drug and the other group something which looks like the drug but in fact contains no active element (called a *placebo*). This is called a *single-blind* experiment. To avoid bias on the part of the doctor, who naturally expects a certain effect from the drug and might unconsciously affect the outcome, a method of distribution might be used so that the doctor doesn't know which group is which. In this case, the experiment is called *double-blind*.

If we are unable to match pairs of people, we might instead take two sufficiently large groups and hope that any differences will balance each other out. We might assign the people totally at random, so that one group is larger than another. Alternatively, we can decide to make the size of the groups equal beforehand and assign the people at random within this framework. Experiments in which the subjects are randomly assigned to groups are examples of *completely randomised design*.

Apart from avoiding unconscious bias, randomisation also shares around the chance effects from outside factors. This is particularly important when we think there is a chance of a *systematic* bias of some kind.

We can take quite a trivial example to illustrate this process. Suppose I'm assigning the numbers 1–9 to three columns and I'm interested in the totals of these columns. The first method I use to assign the numbers is to look at the pages of a book and take the numbers as they come, starting from the front. Of course, this gives me the columns

$$
\begin{array}{ccc}
1 & 4 & 7 \\
2 & 5 & 8 \\
3 & 6 & 9
\end{array}
$$

with column totals 6, 15 and 24 respectively. Being statistically very naive, I might think that this showed that there was a big difference between the columns.

Now suppose that I assign the numbers on the basis of a randomised selection. On p. 227 is a table of random numbers. Before looking at the numbers I decide on the procedure I will follow – write the numbers in the same order as before, taking them as they come, ignoring any 0's or numbers I have already used. The first row of the random numbers starts

$$\underline{8\,6\,1\,3} \quad 8\,\underline{4}\,1\,0 \quad 0\,\underline{7}\,3\,0 \quad 3\,\underline{9}\,0\,\underline{5} \quad 9\,7\,9\,6 \quad 8\,8\,0\,7 \quad 3\,7\,\underline{2}\,6\ldots$$

and so my columns are

8	3	9
6	4	5
1	7	2

with column sums 15, 14 and 16.

On this basis, I might conclude that the columns were likely to be more or less equal!

The point is that the first method introduced a *systematic bias* in the column sums. The second method removed this bias and made a more equal distribution more likely. The widely different column totals from the first method could actually also have resulted from using the second method. This is unlikely, but possible. There is a difference between this much variation happening by chance and happening as a result of faulty experimental design.

A systematic bias might take the form of the time of day, for example. Suppose I ask three volunteers to carry out a test which one does in the morning, the next at lunch time and the third in the afternoon. I note the time taken as 8, 15 and 21 minutes respectively. I carry out the test the next day in the same order, giving 7, 16 and 22, and on the third day, also in the same order, giving 5, 14 and 24 minutes. If I arrange my results in a table, I have

	Operator	
A	B	C
8	15	21
7	16	22
5	14	24
Morning	Lunch	Afternoon

If I add up the columns, I find a big difference. Is the difference in the operator? Not necessarily: it could be that operators work best in the morning, and worst in the afternoon when they're tired. A supposed difference in operator could be due simply to the time of day.

Blocking

Usually when we design an experiment, we are interested in the effect of a particular factor on the response variable. Typical examples would be different varieties of tomatoes having an effect on the resultant yield or the length of time a traffic light is red at a particular junction affecting the length of the queue which builds up. But along with the factor we want to test, there are usually other factors which also have an effect and which we cannot hold constant. The tomatoes would also be affected by the type of soil, the amount of water and sunlight they received, and so on. The traffic queue would also be affected by the time of day – morning rush-hour or lunch time – and the day itself – Monday or Sunday. When we know from previous experience that a particular factor, other than the one we are interested in, is likely to have a significant effect we can apply a procedure called *blocking*. In this way we can remove the effect of this factor from the analysis and make the test for the effect of the experimental factor more sensitive.

Suppose we are interested in the effect of factor A, but know from previous experience that factor B can also have an effect. Blocking aims to divide the experimental area into blocks where the effect of factor B is constant. So if we're interested in the yield of grape-vines but know that their position on the hill affects the yield of a vine, we can divide the plot into a series of strips, or blocks, running across the hill:

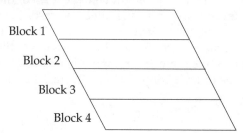

Now the effect of factor B, position on the hillside, is more or less constant within any of these blocks.

Randomised block design

We can distribute our varieties of grapes, say P, Q and R, so that each variety occurs in each of the blocks. The distribution can be randomised by using random numbers. One procedure could be:

- look at a series of random digits, ignoring any 0's
- if the digit is divisible by 3, i.e. 3, 6 or 9, we assign P
- if the digit leaves a remainder of 1 when divided by 3, i.e. 1, 4 or 7, we assign Q
- if the digit leaves a remainder of 2 when divided by 3, i.e. 2, 5 or 8, we assign R.

Since it is the 10th day of the month today, we'll take the 10th row of random numbers from the table. This starts

$$5\,0\,9\,7\,9\,2\,1\,5\,1\,0\,0\,1\,5\,7\,0\,1\ldots$$

5 leaves a remainder of 2, so we assign R
0 we ignore
9 means we assign P

and so the last variety in block 1 is Q.

Block 1
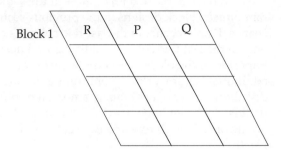

Similarly, starting from where we left off,

7 is Q,   9 is P   so   R to complete Block 2

2 is R,   1 is Q   so   P to complete Block 3

5 is R,   1 is Q   so   P to complete block 4.

So our plot design finally looks like this:

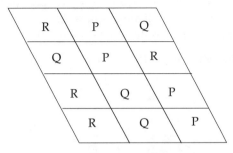

This is an example of a *randomised block design*. We can use it whenever we suspect one particular factor will have an unwanted extra effect. For example, if we thought that the time of day had an effect on an experiment which lasted two hours, we might divide the day into four blocks and assign each type of experiment at random within the blocks.

Block 1	E1	E2	E3	10 am –12 noon
Block 2	E3	E1	E2	12–2 pm
Block 3	E3	E1	E2	2–4 pm
Block 4	E1	E2	E3	4–6 pm

Latin squares

Randomised block design can help when there is one extra factor to take into account, but we may need to deal with the effect of *two* extra factors. We then have to block both of these at the same time. If you look at the two randomised block designs in the previous section, you will see that, just by chance, P only occurs in the last two columns of the first design and E2 only in the last two columns of the second design. This may not be important if the blocks are completely homogenous, but if we suspect an additional factor working from column to column we would like to distribute our varieties equally among the columns as well as the rows. To do this, we assign them to a design called a *Latin square*, where each variety occurs once in each row and each column. For a 3×3 design, it might look like this:

P	Q	R
R	P	Q
Q	R	P

In fact, it has to look something like this. You will find that even if you swap columns or swap rows you will always end up with the same basic design: there will always be a diagonal of just one letter and by swapping letters and/or reflecting you will find yourself back to the same square.

This is not the case with a 4×4 Latin square. Two such examples are

P	Q	R	S
S	P	Q	R
R	S	P	Q
Q	R	S	P

and

P	Q	R	S
S	R	Q	P
Q	P	S	R
R	S	P	Q

and no amount of swapping rows, columns, letters or reflecting will turn one into the other. There are lists of the different squares given in specialised books for experimental design. For a strictly randomised procedure, you should:

- select one of the designs at random
- arrange the rows at random
- arrange the columns at random
- assign each letter to one of the levels of the third factor at random.

For example, I could be conducting an experiment where there were four levels of three factors and I wanted to use a 4×4 Latin square. From a suitable book, I choose at random one of the 4×4 designs, say

R1	P	Q	R	S
R2	S	R	Q	P
R3	Q	P	S	R
R4	R	S	P	Q

Following a random arrangement of the digits 1, 2, 3 and 4, say $2 - 4 - 1 - 3$, I rearrange the rows accordingly:

	C1	C2	C3	C4
R2	S	R	Q	P
R4	R	S	P	Q
R1	P	Q	R	S
R3	Q	P	S	R

I repeat this operation, choosing a further ordering of 1–4, say $3 - 4 - 2 - 1$, and rearrange the columns accordingly to give:

C3	C4	C2	C1
Q	P	R	S
P	Q	S	R
R	S	Q	P
S	R	P	Q

Finally, I assign the letters P, Q, R and S at random to the four levels of the third factor – for example, P is operator 2, Q is operator 1, R is operator 4 and S is operator 3.

<table>
<tr><td>**Example**</td><td>An agricultural research station wishes to investigate the effect of ploughing depth and type of fertiliser on the yield of three varieties of wheat. It has available one large field and three types of fertiliser and can plough to three different depths.</td></tr>
</table>

(a)   Design a suitable small experiment for this investigation

(b)   Comment briefly on any practical considerations which need to be borne in mind.

[ULEAC 1996]

Solution   Divide the field up into three equal strips in one direction: these can be blocks for ploughing depths. Divide the field up in the other direction into three equal strips: these can be the blocks for fertilisers.

Now for assigning the varieties: toss a coin to decide whether to choose the design

A	B	C
C	A	B
B	C	A

or its mirror image

C	B	A
B	A	C
A	C	B

Then assign V_1, V_2 and V_3 at random to A, B and C using random numbers or a similar method, to arrive at the experimental design. It may be like this, for example.

		Fertilisers		
		F1	F2	F3
	D1	V_3	V_1	V_2
Ploughing depths	D2	V_1	V_2	V_3
	D3	V_2	V_3	V_1

It's obviously more convenient to plough all of one third of the field to one depth, another third to another depth, and so on, rather than chop and change between sub-blocks. This assumes that the field has the same fertility, amount of sun and equivalent drainage throughout. If you had serious doubts about this, you might further divide the field into a number of sub-plots and carry out the same procedure within each. You would have to make sure you knew which to apply first – the ploughing or the fertiliser!

The model assumes that the effects of the depths and fertilisers are independent. You would have to be confident that one particular fertiliser was not more effective when combined with one particular depth, for example. In this case, there is said to be no *interaction* between the factors. If there is interaction, or we suspect that there might be, we would have to revise the experimental design and analysis.

EXERCISES

1 Write short notes on:

(a) assumptions

(b) sample size

(c) experimental error

(d) replication

(e) response variable

(f) randomisation

(g) blocking

(h) randomised block design

(i) Latin squares.

2 A factory is to introduce a new product which will be assembled from a number of components. Three different designs are considered and four employees are asked to compare their speed of assembly. The trial is carried out one morning and each of the four employees assembled design *A* from 8.30 am to 9.30 am, design *B* from 10.00 am to 11.00 am and design *C* from 11.30 am to 12.30 pm. The number of products completed by each of the employees is shown in the following table.

Design	Employee			
	1	2	3	4
A	17	4	38	8
B	21	6	52	20
C	28	9	64	22

Comment on the fact that all employees assembled the designs in the same order. Suggest a better way of carrying out the experiment.

[AEB 1991]

3 The running costs of three different types of coal-fired central heating are to be compared. A coal merchant identifies 16 houses, each with one of the three types of central heating. He records how much the occupier spends on coal between November and February.

		Expenditure on coal, £
	A	96, 49, 110, 146
Type of central heating	*B*	173, 67, 59, 94, 87, 142, 86
	C	210, 157, 53, 99, 194

Suggest improvements to the data collection and/or design of the experiment which would increase the chance of detecting differences between types of central heating, if such differences exist.

[AEB 1995]

4 The manager of a bicycle shop wishes to compare the performance of two makes of tyre. He advertises that anyone buying a tyre of either make during the next week will be given a free inner tube. However they must agree to note the length of time from the new tyre being put on until it sustains a puncture.

The following data were collected.

Make of tyre	Number of days to puncture
A	43, 155, 3, 167, 212, 142, 12, 96, 78, 191, 77
B	23, 144, 34, 22

Comment on the method of data collection, the appropriateness of the variable measured, the sample sizes and on any other matters relevant to the experiment.

[AEB 1994]

5 A hospital doctor wished to compare the effectiveness of four brands of painkiller *A, B, C* and *D*. She arranged that when patients on a surgical ward requested painkillers they would be asked if their pain was mild, severe or very severe. The first patient who said mild would be given brand *A*, the second who said mild brand *B*, the third brand *C* and the fourth brand *D*. Painkillers would be allocated in the same way to the first four patients who said their pain was severe and to the first four patients who said their pain was very severe.

The patients were then asked to record the time, in minutes, for which the painkillers were effective.

The following data were collected.

Brand	*A*	*B*	*C*	*D*
mild	165	214	173	155
severe	193	292	142	211
very severe	107	110	193	212

Criticise the experiment and suggest improvements.

[AEB 1994]

SUMMARY

When you have finished this section you should

- appreciate that an experiment allows a cause to be established

- know that to compare the mean values, we need to have an estimate of the underlying variance

- know that we can form this estimate if we run a series of experiments where all the conditions are constant

- know that this is not possible in general and that we have to use more sophisticated methods

- be familiar with the terms used in experimental design and their meanings

- know that randomisation reduces bias and makes the effect of the factor in which we are interested more evident

- know the purpose of randomised blocking where more than one factor is operating

- be familiar with the structure of Latin squares

- know that these are used when the effects of three factors are being considered.

6

Control charts and acceptance sampling

In this section we look at two important and commonly used techniques for quality control.

Control charts are used for monitoring the output of mass-production processes. They are intended to ensure that the production process is stable and the quality of the output is within certain tolerance limits. In acceptance sampling, random samples are taken from batches of a product and on the evidence gained from examining the sample, decisions are made about whether to accept or reject the batch.

At the end of this section you should be able to:

● construct and interpret a control chart, both for the mean and for the fraction defective

● know the meaning of action and warning limits and be able to find them

● understand single and double sampling plans.

Control charts

Consider a factory producing metal cylinders of diameter 2 cm. These are then despatched to other factories which use them as components of their manufacturing processes.

No mass-production process is able to produce items which are consistently exactly 2 cm in diameter. It is more likely that the diameters will have a normal distribution with mean close to 2 cm and a certain variance, which should be small. The factory producing the cylinders obviously wishes to keep its customers happy, so to maintain output within acceptable limits it has a system of *quality control*. *Quality control* is the inspection procedure at the factory which is designed to ensure that the value of the mean stays reasonably close to its intended value. Small random samples are taken from the output at regular intervals and the sample means are plotted on a *control chart*.

This is a way of determining whether the production process is under control or whether action needs to be taken (to adjust machinery, for example). Other situations in which this method might be profitably used are:

- in the chemical industry where purity of the product is important

- in seed production where germination rates are significant

- in the manufacture of packaging materials where strength and resilience are important considerations.

Indeed, quality control is an important aspect of most mass-production processes.

The theory behind control charts

The essential idea of a control chart is based around the concept of a confidence interval. We will follow a general account with some practical examples to illustrate the theory.

Suppose a factory is producing goods with a single, measurable, quantitative variable (for example, length, weight or lifetime) which is assumed to have a normal distribution with mean μ. In an ideal world every item would come off the production line with this value. In the real world, for a variety of reasons, there will be some variability in the goods produced. Consumers expect some variability – nobody expects to find exactly 500 ml of liquid in a 500 ml carton of drink bought in the local supermarket, but they would expect it to be close to 500 ml. A common procedure is to use a quality control chart which, as well as including the value of μ, has *warning limits* and *action limits*.

Warning limits are often drawn at a 95% interval around the mean value. These would be calculated from the formula

$$\mu \pm \frac{(1.96)\,(\sigma)}{\sqrt{n}} \qquad \text{(95\% interval)}$$

Action limits might be drawn at a 99.8% interval around the mean value and would be calculated from

$$\mu \pm \frac{(3.09)\,(\sigma)}{\sqrt{n}} \qquad \text{(99.8\% interval)}$$

Note that $\quad \mu \pm \dfrac{(2)\,(\sigma)}{\sqrt{n}}$ and $\mu \pm \dfrac{(3)\,(\sigma)}{\sqrt{n}}$

provide very good approximations to these limits and are commonly used in practice. They illustrate the 2-σ and 3-σ rules, namely that approximately 95% of any normal distribution lies within two standard deviations either side of the mean and that approximately 99.8% of any normal distribution lies within three standard deviations either side of the mean (see Figure 6.1).

Figure 6.1

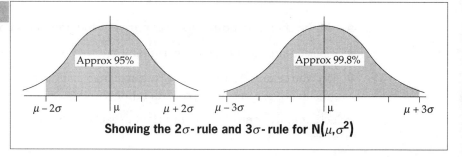

Showing the 2σ-rule and 3σ-rule for N(μ,σ^2)

The values of 95% and 99.8% for warning and action limits, respectively, although common, are not always used. Other values will be used in the exercises that follow. The principle remains the same though, and all that will change in the formulae given is the multiple of $\dfrac{\sigma}{\sqrt{n}}$.

A typical control chart for a mean value will consist of five lines – the control line at μ, and lines placed symmetrically on either side of it at 95% (warning limits) and 99.8% (action limits). (See Figure 6.2.)

Figure 6.2

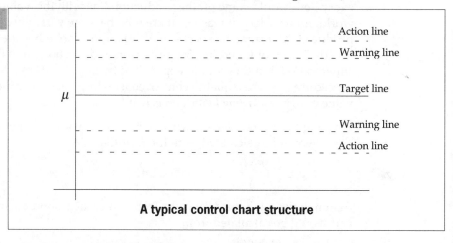

A typical control chart structure

Before the control chart can be constructed, a value for σ (the population standard deviation) has to be found. Typically, a working value for this would be calculated from a large random sample from the production line (when production is taking place under very controlled conditions). In exam questions this will usually be given; if not, sufficient information will be given for you to find it.

A value for n, the size of samples, will be taken once the monitoring process begins. Usually, samples will be fairly small (e.g. $n = 5$) so that the monitoring can proceed quickly and any faults which are found can be corrected quickly.

If 95% warning limits are used, then in the long run we would expect that only 5% of the sample means would lie outside the warning limits. This means that 1 in 20 of the sample means lying outside the warning limits but within the action limits would be considered acceptable.

At 99.8% action limits we would expect (in the long run) to find only 0.2% of the sample means outside these limits. This means that 1 in 500 of the sample mean values above or below the action lines would be acceptable, but any more than this would require action to be taken.

Example　A machine is designed to dispense 500 ml of a brand of soft drink into cartons. Evidence from a large sample has given a value of 1.4 ml for the standard deviation. The process is monitored by taking regular random samples of eight cartons from the production line. Find 95% warning limits and 99% action limits for this process.

Solution　The limits are calculated from

$$\mu \pm \frac{(z)\,(\sigma)}{\sqrt{n}}$$

where for 95% warning limits the value of z can be found from normal distribution tables and correspond to Figure 6.3.

Figure 6.3

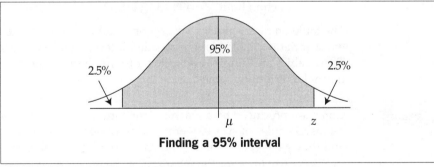

Finding a 95% interval

Tables give $z = 1.96$.

For the 99% action limits, Figure 6.4 provides the appropriate value of z.

Figure 6.4

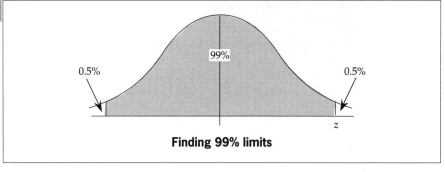

Finding 99% limits

Tables give $z = 2.5758$.

The 95% limits are therefore

$$500 \pm \frac{(1.9600)\,(1.4)}{\sqrt{8}}$$

i.e. upper warning limit = 500.97

lower warning limit = 499.03 (2 d.p.)

and the 99% limits are

$$500 \pm \frac{(2.5758)\,(1.4)}{\sqrt{8}}$$

i.e. upper action limit   = 501.27

lower action limit   = 498.73 (2 d.p.)

The table on p. 229 gives z-values for a number of often-used intervals, e.g. 95% (under $p = 0.0250$ for a two-sided interval) and 99% (under $p = 0.0050$). These tables are simpler and quicker to use than the more comprehensive normal distribution tables.

Coins are produced by a machine; the target mass for the coins is 12.5 grams. Samples of size 10 were randomly selected from the production line and they gave values for Σx_i and Σx_i^2 shown in the table. Calculate 95% and 99.8% control lines for the means. Plot the means on the control chart and comment on the current state of the process.

Sample number	1	2	3	4	5	6	7	8
Σx_i	124.8	125.3	125.9	123.7	124.9	128.3	126.1	127.5
Σx_i^2	1588.6	1586.1	1601.8	1628.4	1580.9	1581.4	1583.4	1588.7

We use the fact that 80 items have been sampled in all to find an estimate of the population standard deviation.

From the table

Grand total $\Sigma x_i = 1006.5$

Grand total $\Sigma x_i^2 = 12739.3$

Hence $\bar{x} = \dfrac{1006.5}{80} = 12.58$ (2 d.p.)

The unbiased estimate of the variance is

$$s^2 = \frac{80}{79}\left(\frac{12739.3}{80} - \left(\frac{1006.5}{80}\right)^2\right)$$

$$\Rightarrow \quad s = 0.9826 \quad \text{(4 d.p)}$$

95% lines are at $12.58 \pm \dfrac{(1.96)\,(0.9826)}{\sqrt{10}}$

99.8% lines are at $12.58 \pm \dfrac{(3.09)\,(0.9826)}{\sqrt{10}}$

giving   95% at   (11.97, 13.19)

99.8% at (11.62 13.54)

The control chart with the means of the eight samples plotted is shown on the next page.

The evidence of the first eight samples suggests that the process is well under control.

There are no points outside the warning limits and no discernible trend either upwards or downwards in the values of the sample means.

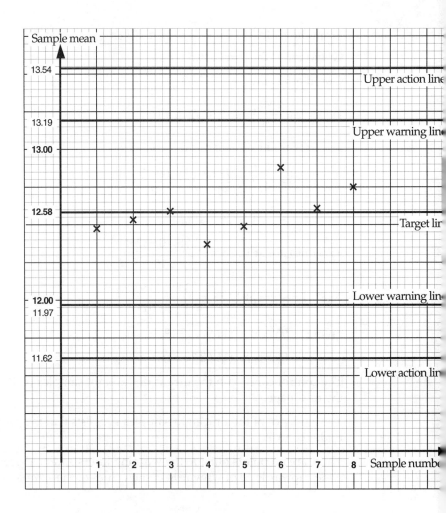

Control charts for fraction defective

The theory and examples so far have dealt with situations in which the variable in question had a quantitative value (i.e. the mean). It could be, though, that an item is either good or bad. A slightly different approach is required when we are testing a qualitative variable – whether items coming off a production line are in working order or defective.

In the mass-production of a certain item, the probability of an individual item being defective (i.e. unsuitable for further use) is p. In practice, this value would be estimated from previous experience of the manufacturing process by examining samples obtained when the process is working as well as it can. The production is monitored by taking regular random samples of size n. Now the number of defectives in such a sample has the distribution

$$X \sim B(n,p)$$

Providing n is sufficiently large, the sample proportion will be approximately distributed as

$$N\left(p, \frac{p(1-p)}{n}\right)$$

(This result was derived in Section 1 of *Statistics 2*.)

It then follows that 95% and 99.8% confidence limits for the sample proportion are

$$p \pm (1.96) \sqrt{\frac{p(1-p)}{n}} \qquad (95\%)$$

$$p \pm (3.09) \sqrt{\frac{p(1-p)}{n}} \qquad (99.8\%)$$

and these will provide the warning and action limits, respectively. The sample proportion is the proportion of items defective in a sample of size n, or *fraction defective* as it is usually called in this context. As before, the values 95% and 99.8% are very common but not immutable – variations will occur in examples. Only the numbers 1.96 and 3.09 will change in the above formulae.

Example

Eight samples of size 100 are taken from a production line and the number of defectives in each sample is shown in the table.

Sample no.	1	2	3	4	5	6	7	8
No. of defectives	6	8	5	2	6	7	4	8

Draw up a control chart for the fraction defective showing 95% and 99.8% control lines.

Solution

Total number of defectives in the eight samples $= 46$

$$\text{Proportion defective} = \frac{46}{800} = 0.0575$$

95% warning units at

$$0.0575 \pm (1.96) \sqrt{\frac{(0.0575)(0.9425)}{100}}$$

i.e. at $\quad 0.0575 \pm 0.04563$

i.e. at $\quad 0.0119 \text{ and } 0.1031$

99.8% action limits at

$$0.0575 \pm (3.09) \sqrt{\frac{(0.0575)\,(0.9425)}{100}}$$

i.e. at 0.0575 ± 0.07193

i.e. at -0.0144 and 0.1294

The last of these clearly represents an impossibility and occurs as a result of the use of a normal approximation to the binomial distribution. It is therefore not used.

The proportion of defectives in each of the individual samles is plotted on the control chart shown below. For example, for the first sample, the proportion of defectives is $\frac{6}{100} = 0.06$.

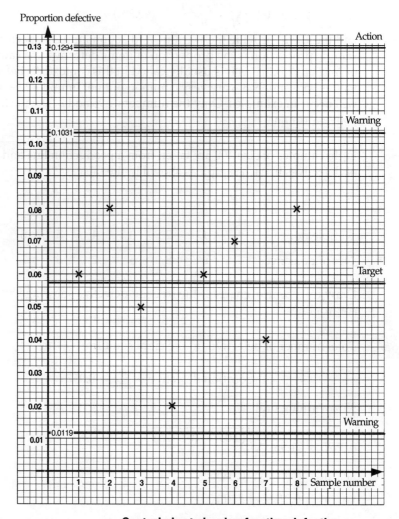

Control chart showing fraction defective

The control chart shows the lower warning line. However, in practice, the quality control team would not be concerned if the proportion of defectives fell below this line since this would mean that the number of defectives per sample had fallen below the acceptable level.

It is not necessary for samples to be of the same size, as the next example shows.

Example

Items from a production line are regularly sampled and the first 10 samples gave the following number of defectives per sample:

Sample no.	1	2	3	4	5	6	7	8	9	10
Sample size	220	350	280	250	310	300	280	300	250	280
No. of defectives	26	28	24	28	31	29	25	26	30	24

Draw up a control chart for the fraction defective showing 95% and 98% control lines.

Solution

Total number of items sampled $= 2820$

Total number of defectives $= 271$

Proportion defective (p) $= 0.0961$ (4 d.p.)

To find a value for n we use the average size of the first ten samples

$$n = 2820 \div 10$$
$$= 282$$

95% warning limits are

$$0.0961 \pm 1.96 \sqrt{\frac{(0.0961)\,(0.9039)}{282}}$$

i.e. at 0.0961 ± 0.0344

i.e. at 0.0617 and 0.1305

98% action limits are

$$0.0961 \pm 2.3263 \sqrt{\frac{(0.0961)\,(0.9039)}{282}}$$

i.e. at 0.0961 ± 0.0408

i.e. at 0.0553 and 0.1369

giving the following control chart (showing the first 10 sample proportions).

As in the previous example, we would not be concered if the proportion of defectives fell below the average value of 0.0961, and so only the upper warning and action limits are shown.

The sample proportions are calculated, for example, by

$$\frac{26}{220} = 0.12 \text{ (2 d.p.)} \qquad \frac{28}{350} = 0.08 \text{ (2 d.p.) and so on.}$$

Proportion defective

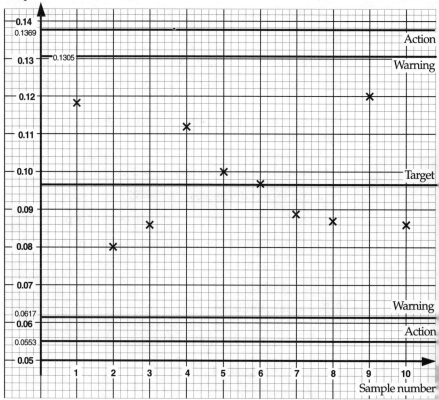

The control chart shows that the process is performing within the acceptable limits so far.

Control charts are also used to monitor the standard deviation or range of samples of production. These are constructed in a similar way but are not part of the 'A' level syllabus, so we will not look at them here.

You should now be able to complete Exercises 1–4 on pp. 99–100.

Acceptance sampling

Consumers or purchasers of mass-produced items (including other factories buying in components, or wholesale distributors), will normally receive these in large *batches* or consignments. Since it is impractical and expensive to test every item in a batch, a standard procedure is to take one or more samples from a batch and test the items in the sample(s). In a *single-stage sampling plan*, just one sample is taken from a batch and the decision about whether to accept the batch is made on the basis of the number of defectives found in the sample.

Example

Components arrive at a factory in batches of 1000. Each batch is tested according to the following procedure. A random sample of 25 items is taken from each batch and tested. A batch is rejected if more than one defective item is found in the sample. If the probability of an individual item being defective is p, find in terms of p the probability of accepting the batch and evaluate this in the case when $p = 0.04$.

Solution

For the sample of size 25, the number of defectives X in the sample has a binomial distribution since there is a fixed number of trials (25), a fixed probability of an item being defective (p), and presumably the trials are independent – we have no reason to believe otherwise.

The number of defectives $X \sim B(25, p)$

Decision rule: accept batch if $X \le 1$

Therefore probability (acceptance)

$$
\begin{aligned}
&= P(X = 0) + P(X = 1) \\
&= (1 - p)^{25} + 25p(1 - p)^{24} \\
&= (1 - p)^{24}(1 - p + 25p) \\
&= (1 - p)^{24}(1 + 24p)
\end{aligned}
$$

If $p = 0.04$ then the batch will be accepted with probability

$$
\begin{aligned}
&(1 - 0.04)^{24}(1 + (24)(0.04)) \\
&= 0.7358 \quad \text{(4 d.p.)}
\end{aligned}
$$

A second method of acceptance sampling is the *double-sampling plan*. Here a first sample is taken (of size n_1) and on the basis of evidence of this sample the batch may be

● rejected outright

● accepted outright

● re-sampled (with sample size n_2) and the evidence from the second or *both* samples used to decide whether to reject the batch.

How this works is best seen from an example.

Example

Large batches of components are received by a factory. The factory operates a double-sampling plan for accepting each batch based on the following rules.

A sample of size 50 is taken from the batch and if it contains no defective items the batch is accepted. If it contains more than one defective item the batch is rejected. If it contains one defective item, a further sample of size 50 is taken and the batch is accepted if the combined sample of 100 has no more than one defective item. If, for these particular components, the probability of an item being defective is p, find in terms of p the probability of accepting a batch and evaluate this when $p = 0.002$.

Solution

The number of defectives in a sample of size 50 is $X \sim B(50,p)$.

The batch is accepted if

(a)   the first sample of size 50 has $X < 1$

or

(b)   the combined sample of size 100 has $X \le 1$

This can happen if sample 1 has one defective item and sample 2 has no defective items.

A second sample is taken only if the first sample includes a single defective item.

Hence probability of acceptance

$$= (1-p)^{50} \qquad + \qquad 50p(1-p)^{49}(1-p)^{50}$$

$$\underbrace{\begin{Bmatrix} \text{1st sample} \\ \text{has 0} \\ \text{defectives} \end{Bmatrix}}_{} \quad \text{or} \quad \underbrace{\begin{Bmatrix} \text{1st sample} \\ \text{has 1} \\ \text{defective} \end{Bmatrix}}_{} \underbrace{\begin{Bmatrix} \text{2nd sample} \\ \text{has 0} \\ \text{defectives} \end{Bmatrix}}_{}$$

$$= (1-p)^{50}\left(1 + 50p(1-p)^{49}\right)$$

When $p = 0.002$ this expression gives the value

Probability (acceptance) $= 0.9868$ (4 d.p.)

Example

A firm is to introduce an acceptance sampling scheme. Three alternative plans are considered.

Plan A

Take a sample of 50 and accept the batch if no defectives are found, otherwise reject the batch.

Plan B

Take a sample of 50 and accept the batch if two or fewer defectives are found, otherwise reject the batch.

Plan C

Take a sample of 40 and accept the batch if no defectives are found. Reject the batch if two or more defectives are found. If one defective is found, then take a further sample of size 40. If a total of two or fewer defectives (out of 80) is found, accept the batch, otherwise reject it.

(a) Find the probability of acceptance for each of the plans A, B and C if batches are submitted containing

    (i)   1% defective

    (ii)   10% defective

(b) Show that for batches containing 1% defective items, the average number of items inspected using plan C is similar to the number inspected using plans A or B.

[AEB 1993]

Solution

(a) For samples of size 50

$$X \sim B(50, p)$$

For plan A

$$P(\text{acceptance}) = (1 - p)^{50}$$

and if $p = 0.01$ we get 0.6050 (4 d.p.)

       if $p = 0.1$ we get 0.0052 (4 d.p.)

For plan B

$$
\begin{aligned}
P(\text{acceptance}) &= (1-p)^{50} + \binom{50}{1}p(1-p)^{49} + \binom{50}{2}p^2(1-p)^{48} \\
&= (1-p)^{50} + 50p(1-p)^{49} + 1225p^2(1-p)^{48} \\
&= (1-p)^{48}\left[(1-p)^2 + 50p(1-p) + 1225p^2\right] \\
&= (1-p)^{48}\left[1176p^2 + 48p + 1\right]
\end{aligned}
$$

If $p = 0.01$ we get   0.9862

If $p = 0.1$ we get   0.1117

Under plan C, the batch will be accepted in the following circumstances:

If $X = 0$ for $X \sim B(40, p)$

or   if $X = 1$ for $X \sim B(40, p)$

and *then* $X = 1$ or 0 for $X \sim B(40, p)$

since we must take *at most* two defectives from both samples combined.

Hence probability(acceptance under plan C)

$$= (1-p)^{40} + \left(40p(1-p)^{39}\right)\left((1-p)^{40} + 40p(1-p)^{39}\right)$$

which gives

$$(1-p)^{40}\left[1 + 40p(1-p)^{39} + 1600p^2(1-p)^{38}\right]$$

and when $p = 0.01$ we get   0.9228 (4 d.p.)

$$p = 0.10 \quad \text{we get} \quad 0.0201 \text{ (4 d.p.)}$$

(b)   Under plan C, either 40 or 80 items will be sampled.

40 items are sampled if no defectives are found.

80 items are sampled if one defective is found in the first sample of 40.

Hence

P(number sampled = 40)
= P(no defectives found)   = $(0.99)^{40}$
P(number sampled = 80)
= P(1 defective is found) = $(40)\,(0.01)\,(0.99)^{39}$

Hence expected number of items sampled

$$= (40)\,(0.99)^{40} + (80)\,(40)\,(0.01)\,(0.99)^{39}$$
$$= 48.4 \quad \text{(1 d.p.)}$$

and this is near to the numbers sampled in plans A and B.

Note that the expressions obtained for P(acceptance) in these examples are called *operating characteristics* for the respective schemes. The graph of p against P(acceptance) is called the *operating characteristic graph*.

You should now be able to complete the exercises below.

EXERCISES

1 Samples of size nine are taken from a production line at regular intervals. The target mean for the process is 25 and the standard deviation is 0.4. Calculate 95% and 98% control lines for the process.

2 A machine is set to fill capsules with a particular drug. The distribution of the weights of the fillings is specified to be the normal distribution with mean 12.00 g and standard deviation 0.35 g.

(a) Using graph paper, draw a control chart for the sample mean, indicating 98% warning limits and 99% action limits, assuming samples of size 10 will be taken.

(b) On three separate occasions when the chart was in use, the following values of the mean of samples of size 10 were recorded.
(i) 12.27   (ii) 11.68   (iii) 12.17

In each case plot the point on your chart and in each case comment on the state of the filling process.

On another occasion when the chart was in use, a sample of size 10 was taken and the variance of this sample was found to be 0.12 g^2.

(c) Calculate a 95% confidence interval for the variance of the population of fillings from which this sample was taken.

[ULEAC 1996]

3 At a factory making ball bearings, a scoop is used to take a sample at regular intervals. All the ball bearings in the scoop are classified as defective or not defective according to whether or not they fit two gauges. This is a very quick and easy test to carry out.

The numbers in the scoop and the numbers defective are shown below for ten scoops at a time when production was thought to be satisfactory.

Number in scoop	95	99	115	120	84	107	97	119	92	112
Number defective	16	6	11	10	11	5	13	14	10	13

(a) Use the data to estimate p, the proportion defective and n, the average number in a scoop. Use these estimated values of n and p to set up a control chart for the fraction defective. Show approximate 95% and 99.8% upper and lower limits.
Plot the 10 samples on the chart and comment.

(b) The following samples occurred on separate occasions when the chart was in operation:

(i) number in scoop 115 number defective 21
(ii) number in scoop 94 number defective 8
(iii) number in scoop 92 number defective 20
(iv) number in scoop 12 number defective 3
(v) number in scoop 104 number defective 1

For each of the above samples, plot a point on the chart and comment on the current state of the process and on what action, if any, is necessary.

[AEB 1991]

4 A company owns a large number of supermarkets. Deliveries are made each day from a central warehouse to the supermarkets. Each week, 80 deliveries are monitored and the number which are unsatisfactory (either late or incomplete) is recorded.

During a period when the service as a whole was regarded as satisfactory the following data were collected.

Week	1	2	3	4	5	6	7	8	9	10
Number unsatisfactory	14	9	12	15	8	10	18	11	19	15

(a) Use the data above to estimate p, the proportion of unsatisfactory deliveries. Use this estimate to calculate upper and lower warning and action limits for a control chart for p. There should be a chance of approximately 1 in 40 of violating each warning limit and approximately 1 in 1000 of violating each action limit if p remains unchanged. Draw the control chart and plot the 10 points corresponding to the data in the table. (Allow space for at least 14 points and for values of p up to 0.4.)

(b) The following numbers of unsatisfactory deliveries were recorded on separate occasions when the chart was in use.

(i) 22
(ii) 18
(iii) 27
(iv) 2

For each of the occasions above, plot a point on your chart and comment on the current state of deliveries.

(c) If in a particular week the probability of each delivery being unsatisfactory is 0.32, what is the probability of the number recorded exceeding the upper action limit?

[AEB 1994]

5 (a) Dishwasher powder is dispensed into cartons by machines. The distribution of powder dispensed is normal with mean 2.0 kg and standard deviation 42 g.

   (i) Set up and draw a control chart for the sample mean, indicating 95% warning limits and 99% action limits, assuming random samples of size nine will be taken.

   The quality manager responsible for the machine takes eight random samples, each of nine cartons, and the mean amounts of powder dispensed for these samples are as follows:

Sample number	1	2	3	4	5	6	7	8
Mean (kg)	2.005	1.993	2.003	2.012	2.017	2.022	2.020	2.025

   (ii) Plot these means on your control chart.

   (iii) Comment on the pattern revealed on your chart and advise the manager of any action needed.

   (b) Before dispensing the dishwasher powder into the cartons, batches of empty cartons must be checked for suitability in terms of printing, shape, etc. Any defective cartons will be rejected. The quality manager intends to introduce an acceptance sampling scheme and considers two possibilities.

   A: Take a random sample of 50 cartons and accept the batch if two or fewer defective cartons are found, otherwise reject the batch.

   B: Take a random sample of 40 cartons and accept the batch if no defectives are found, and reject the batch if two or more defective cartons are found. If one defective carton is found, then take a further sample of size 40 and if a total of two or fewer defectives from the total sample of 80 is found accept the batch, otherwise reject it.

The quality manager is assured by the carton supplier that batches contain only 2% defective cartons.

Find the probability of acceptance associated with each of the above sampling schemes.

[ULEAC Specimen paper T3]

6 Thatcher's Pottery produces large batches of coffee mugs decorated with the faces of famous politicians. They are considering adopting one of the following sampling plans for batch inspection.

Method A (single sample plan): Select 10 mugs from the batch at random and accept the batch if two or fewer are defective, otherwise reject the batch.

Method B (double sample plan): Select five mugs from the batch at random and accept the batch if there are no defectives, reject the batch if there are two or more defectives, otherwise select another five mugs at random. When the second sample is drawn, count the number of defectives in the combined sample of 10 and accept the batch if the number of defectives is two or fewer, otherwise reject the batch.

(a) If the proportion of defectives in a batch is p, find, in terms of p, for each method in turn, the probability that the batch will be accepted.

(b) Evaluate *both* the above probabilities for $p = 0.2$ and $p = 0.5$.

(c) Hence, or otherwise, decide which of these two plans is more appropriate, and why.

[AEB 1981]

7 When checking large batches of goods the following acceptance sampling plans have similar operating characteristics.

Plan 1: Take a sample of size 50 and accept the batch if three or fewer defectives are found, otherwise reject it.

Plan 2: Take a sample of size 30, accept the batch if zero or one defectives are found and reject the batch if three or more defectives are found. If exactly two defectives are found, take a further sample of size 30. Accept the batch if a total of four or fewer defectives (out of 60) are found, otherwise reject it.

Using the following table, or otherwise, verify that the two plans have similar probabilities of accepting a batch containing 5% defectives.

The table gives the probability of obtaining r *or more* defectives in n independent trials when the probability of a defective in a single trial is 0.05.

r	$n = 30$	$n = 50$
0	1.0000	1.0000
1	0.7854	0.9231
2	0.4465	0.7206
3	0.1878	0.4595
4	0.0608	0.2396

For the second plan, evaluate the expected number of items inspected each time the plan is used when the proportion defective in the batch is 0, 0.02, 0.05, 0.10 and 1.00. Sketch a graph of the expected number of items inspected against proportion defective in the batch.

What factors should be considered when deciding which of the two plans to use?

[AEB 1984]

8 Large batches of door hinges are produced at regular intervals by the Amalgamated Ironworks in Botherham. Let N be the number of hinges in each batch, and p be the proportion of defectives. The company operates a single sample plan for its batch inspection by selecting 10 hinges at random and accepting the batch if there are two or fewer defectives, otherwise rejecting the batch.

(a)   Show that the probability of accepting a batch is

$$(1-p)^8 \,(1 + 8p + 36p^2).$$

(b)   When a batch is rejected it is not discarded, but instead subjected to 100% inspection and all defectives are replaced. Thus if a batch is rejected, N hinges are inspected, whereas if the batch is accepted only 10 hinges are inspected. If $N = 200$, determine the expected amount of inspection in terms of p, the proportion of defectives. Evaluate your expression for $p = 0.1, 0.2, 0.3$ and comment upon the answers.

[AEB 1983]

SUMMARY

Now that you have completed this section you should:

- understand how control charts help to monitor production processes

- be able to draw up a control chart for a mean and a fraction defective showing warning and action limits

- be able to use the information on a control chart to suggest what action, if any, needs to be taken

- understand how single- and double-sampling plans work.

T4

Advanced Modular Mathematics

7

Probability distributions

In this section we shall look at three new probability distributions. The first is the geometric distribution and the second an extension of this, the negative binomial distribution. In both of these the variable is discrete. The final distribution is the exponential: it is related to the Poisson distribution but since it is concerned with lengths, the variable is continuous.

By the end of this section you should know the meaning and use of:

● the probability function for the geometric distribution

● the probability function for the negative binomial distribution

● the exponential distribution.

Geometric distribution

This distribution is related to the binomial distribution. The conditions for each of these, binomial and geometric, to be an appropriate model for the situation are that:

● there should be a number of independent trials

● for each trial there should be two possible outcomes, which we can call 'success' and 'failure', and

● the probability of a success on any one trial has a constant value, usually written p.

If these conditions are met, then as you know, the probability function for the binomial distribution gives us the probability of a certain number of successes out of a certain number of trials.

If $X \sim B(n, p) \implies P(X = r) = \binom{n}{r} p^r q^{n-r}$, $r = 0, 1, 2, ..., n$

Corresponding to this, the probability function for the geometric distribution gives us the probability of a certain number of trials being necessary in order to score the first 'success'.

If $Y \sim \text{Geo}(p) \implies P(Y = r) = p(1-p)^{r-1}$, $r = 1, 2, ...$

Example	If I roll an unbiased die, find the probability that the first '3' occurs on the

(i)   first throw

(ii)   second throw

(iii)   third throw

(iv)   *r*th throw

Solution	This is actually a geometric distribution with $p = \frac{1}{6}$

(i) $p(3 \text{ on 1st throw}) = \frac{1}{6}$

(ii) $p(\text{1st 3 on 2nd throw}) = p(\text{not 3 on 1st} \cap 3 \text{ on 2nd})$

$$= \frac{5}{6} \times \frac{1}{6}$$

(iii) $p(\text{1st 3 on 3rd throw}) = p(\text{not 3 on 1st or 2nd} \cap 3 \text{ on 3rd})$

$$= \frac{5}{6} \times \frac{5}{6} \times \frac{1}{6} = \left(\frac{5}{6}\right)^2 \times \frac{1}{6}$$

(iv) $p(\text{1st 3 on } r\text{th throw}) = p(\text{not 3 on 1st, 2nd, ...}, (r-1)\text{th} \cap 3 \text{ on } r\text{th})$

$$= \left(\frac{5}{6}\right)^{r-1} \times \frac{1}{6}$$

If you compare these probabilities with those given by the formula for $\text{Geo}(\frac{1}{6})$ you will see that they agree.

Mean and variance

In the next section, on probability generating functions, we shall see how we can use this method to find the mean and variance of the geometric distribution. For the moment, we shall just use the results.

If $X \sim \text{Geo}(p)$, then

$$\text{mean} = E(X) = \frac{1}{p}$$

$$\text{variance} = \text{Var}(X) = \frac{q}{p^2}$$

Example	A woman is waiting for a taxi to come into view so that she can hail it. Explain why the geometric distribution is appropriate to model the number of vehicles she sees up to and including the first taxi.

If 5% of the vehicles in the locality are taxis:

(a)   write down the mean number of vehicles up to and including the first taxi

(b) calculate, giving your answer to three significant figures, the probability that the first taxi she sees is the sixth vehicle to come into view

(c) calculate the probability that the first taxi is among the first six vehicles she sees.

[Oxford 1990]

Solution

For the geometric distribution to be the appropriate model

(i) the trials have to be independent (this means that there is no tendency for the taxis to bunch together, for example)

(ii) there have to be only two outcomes (which there are, taxi or not-a-taxi)

(iii) there should be a constant probability of success (this means that there have to be a large number of cars, so that even though you have seen one taxi the probability of seeing another is still (approximately) the same.

If these conditions are satisfied, then the geometric distribution is the appropriate model since it gives the probability of a certain number of vehicles up to and including the first taxi.

(a) $P(\text{taxi}) = 5\% = \frac{1}{20} = p$

Mean of a geometric distribution is $\frac{1}{p} = \frac{1}{\frac{1}{20}} = 20$. The expected number of cars to include the first taxi is 20.

(b) Using $P(X = r) = p(1 - p)^{r-1}$, where X is the random variable 'the number of vehicles up to and including the first taxi', $r = 6$ and $p = \frac{1}{20}$ gives

$$P(X = 6) = \frac{1}{20} \left(\frac{19}{20}\right)^5 = 0.0387 \text{ (3 sig. figs.)}$$

(c) We now need the probability of at least one taxi among the first six vehicles.

$P(\text{at least one taxi}) = 1 - P(\text{no taxi})$

$$= 1 - \left(\frac{19}{20}\right)^6$$

$$= 0.265 \text{ (3 sig. figs.)}$$

At least

In questions on the geometric distribution, it is fairly common to have a part which asks for the probability of X being at least or less then a certain number – the last part of the previous example, for instance.

If the parameter is p, then

$$\begin{aligned}
P(X \geq n) &= P(\text{all the first } (n-1) \text{ outcomes were 'failures'}) \\
&= (1-p)^{n-1} \\
&= q^{n-1}
\end{aligned}$$

and
$$\begin{aligned}
P(X < n) &= 1 - P(X \geq n) \\
&= 1 - q^{n-1}
\end{aligned}$$

Here are some further examples of questions involving the geometric distribution.

Example

In many board games it is necessary to 'throw a six with an ordinary die' before a player can start the game.

(a)   Write down, as a fraction, the probability of a player

    (i)   starting on the first attempt

    (ii)   not starting until the third attempt

    (iii)   requiring more than three attempts before starting.

What is

    (iv)   the most common number of throws required to obtain a six

    (v)   the mean number of throws required to obtain a six?

(b)   Prove that the probability of a player requiring more than n attempts before starting is $\left(\frac{5}{6}\right)^n$.

(c)   What is the smallest value of n if there is to be at least a 95% chance of starting before the nth attempt?

[Oxford 1988]

Solution

(a)   (i) $P(6 \text{ on 1st attempt}) = \frac{1}{6}$

    (ii) $P(\text{first 6 on 3rd attempt}) = \left(\frac{5}{6}\right)^2 \times \frac{1}{6} = \frac{25}{216}$

    (iii) $P(> 3 \text{ attempts}) = 1 - P(1, 2 \text{ or } 3 \text{ attempts})$

        $P(\text{first 6 on 2nd attempt}) = \frac{5}{6} \times \frac{1}{6} = \frac{5}{36}$

        $\Rightarrow P(> 3 \text{ attempts}) = 1 - \left[\frac{1}{6} + \frac{5}{36} + \frac{25}{216}\right]$

        $= \frac{125}{216} \left(= \left(\frac{5}{6}\right)^3, \text{ see solution to (b)}\right)$

(iv)   The attempt with the greatest probability is actually the first, i.e. the most common number of throws is one.

(v)   The mean for a geometric distribution is $\frac{1}{p}$, i.e. we expect $\frac{1}{\frac{1}{6}} = 6$ throws. (This is not the same as saying that six is the most common number of throws.)

(b)   If the player required more than n attempts, it means that each of the first n throws results in a not-six. Since the probability of a not-six is $\frac{5}{6}$, the probability of the first n throws being not-sixes is $\left(\frac{5}{6}\right)^n$.

(c)   The question is a bit tricky here.

P(starting before the nth attempt)

$= 1 - $ P(requiring at least n attempts)

$= 1 - $ P(requiring more than $(n-1)$ attempts)

$= 1 - \left(\frac{5}{6}\right)^{n-1}$ from above.

We need $1 - \left(\frac{5}{6}\right)^{n-1} \geq 0.95$

$\Rightarrow \left(\frac{5}{6}\right)^{n-1} \leq 0.05$

Taking logs, $(n-1) \log \frac{5}{6} \leq \log 0.05$

$\Rightarrow (n-1) \geq \dfrac{\log 0.05}{\log \frac{5}{6}} = 16.4$

$\Rightarrow n \geq 17.4$

least integer is 18

Example

Arnold is a golfer, and believes that, once his ball reaches the green, there is a probability of $\frac{1}{4}$ that he will get the ball into the hole on each subsequent shot. The random variable X represents the number of shots Arnold requires to get the ball into the hole, after he gets the ball on to the green.

(a)   Calculate the probability that X is at least 4.

(b)   Write down E(X).

(c)   State the mode of X.

(d)   Comment on any likely inadequacies in Arnold's model.

[ULEAC 1996]

111

| Solution | The model that is used here is that of a geometric distribution. |

(a) $P(X \geq 4) = 1 - P(X = 1, 2 \text{ or } 3)$

(Note that X cannot take the value of 0.)

$P(X = 1) = \frac{1}{4} : P(X = 2) = \frac{3}{4} \times \frac{1}{4} : P(X = 3) = \left(\frac{3}{4}\right)^2 \times \frac{1}{4}$

$\Rightarrow P(X \geq 4) = 1 - \left[\frac{1}{4} + \frac{3}{16} + \frac{9}{64}\right]$

$= 1 - \frac{37}{64} = \frac{27}{64} \left(= \left(\frac{3}{4}\right)^3\right)$

We could also have stated simply that $P(X \geq 4) = q^3$ to give the same result.

(b) Since X has a geometric distribution, with $p = \frac{1}{4}$,

$$E(X) = \frac{1}{p} = \frac{1}{\frac{1}{4}} = 4$$

(c) The most likely value for any geometric distribution is 1, i.e. the mode is 1.

(d) The outcome of each shot is not independent of the last shot. Also, the probabilities are not constant. In fact, you would expect the probability of holing on the second shot to be greater than on the first since you would expect the ball to be closer to the hole. This contradicts the value of the mode found in (c).

| Example | A darts player practises throwing a dart at the bull's-eye on a dart board. Independently for each throw, her probability of hitting the bull's-eye is 0.2. Let X be the number of throws she makes, up to and including her first success. |

(a) Find the probability that she is successful for the first time on her third throw.

(b) Write down the distribution of X, and give the name of this distribution.

(c) Find the probability that she will have at least three failures before her first success.

(d) Show that the mean value of X is 5.

(You may assume the result

$$\sum_{r=1}^{\infty} rq^{r=1} = \frac{1}{(1-q)^2} \text{ when } |q| < 1.)$$

(e) On another occasion the player throws the dart at the bull's-eye until she has two successes. Let Y be the number of throws she makes up to and including her second success. Given that $\text{Var}(X) = 20$, determine the mean and the variance of Y, and find the probability that $Y = 4$.

[ULEAC 1988]

Solution

(a) P(successful for first time on third throw)

= P(not successful on first two throws $\cap$ successful on third)

= $(0.8)^2 \times 0.2 = 0.128$

(b) This can be modelled by the geometric distribution, since the trials are independent with constant probability.

$$P(X = r) = 0.2 \times 0.8^{r-1} \ (r = 1, 2, \ldots)$$

(c) $P(X \geq 4) = q^3 = 0.8^3 = 0.512$

(d) Here is one way of showing this result. We shall see later, in the relevant section, how we could use probability generating functions for this.

$$E(X) = \sum_{r=1}^{\infty} X_r p_r = \sum_{r=1}^{\infty} r \times P(X = r)$$

$$= \sum_{r=1}^{\infty} rp(1-p)^{r-1} = p \sum_{r=1}^{\infty} r(1-p)^{r-1}$$

$$= p \sum_{r=1}^{\infty} rq^{r-1}$$

We can take p outside the summation, since it is constant. Using the given result,

$$E(X) = p \times \frac{1}{(1-q)^2} = p \times \frac{1}{p^2} \text{ since } 1-q = p$$

$$= \frac{1}{p}$$

Since $p = 0.2$, the mean value for X, $E(X) = \frac{1}{0.2} = 5$

(e) Since $\text{Var}(X) = \frac{q}{p^2}$ and $p = 0.2$, $q = 0.8$,

$$\text{Var}(X) = \frac{0.8}{0.2^2} = 20$$

The time up to and including her first success has a geometric distribution with $p = 0.2$. Since the attempts are independent, she then starts again trying to hit the bull with the same probability of success as before. So the waiting time up to and including the second success (from the first success) is again a geometric distribution with $p = 0.2$. This means that the random variable Y is in fact the sum of two independent random variables, X_1 and X_2, both of which have geometric distributions with $p = 0.2$.

Then
$$E(Y) = E(X_1 + X_2) \qquad = E(X_1) + E(X_2)$$
$$= 2E(X) = 2 \times 5 = 10$$
$$\text{Var}(Y) = \text{Var}(X_1 + X_2) = \text{Var}(X_1) + \text{Var}(X_2)$$
$$= 20 + 20 = 40$$

$$P(Y = 4) = P(B\bar{B}\bar{B}B \text{ or } \bar{B}B\bar{B}B \text{ or } \bar{B}\bar{B}BB)$$

where B means a bull and $\bar{B}$ a not-bull.

$$\Rightarrow P(Y = 4) = 3 \times 0.8^2 \times 0.2^3 = 0.0768$$

The distribution of Y is in fact *negative binomial*. We shall be looking at this type of distribution as our next topic. For the moment, you might like to try Exercises 1–7 at the end of the section.

Negative binomial distribution

This distribution is an extension of the geometric distribution that we have just looked at. Instead of the number of trials before the first success, we are interested in the number of trials before the kth success. Assuming that the necessary conditions apply, if Y is the number of trials up to and including the kth success, then

$$P(Y = n) = P\big((k - 1) \text{ successes in } (n - 1) \text{ trials and } k\text{th success on } n\text{th trial}\big)$$

$$= P\big((k - 1) \text{ successes in } (n - 1) \text{ trials}\big)$$
$$\times P(k\text{th success on } n\text{th trial}) \qquad [\text{since independent}]$$

$$= \text{Arrangements of } (k - 1) \text{ successes in } (n - 1) \text{ trials}$$
$$\times \ P(\text{particular arrangement}) \times p$$

$$= \binom{n-1}{k-1} \times p^{k-1} (1 - p)^{(n-1)-(k-1)} \times p$$

$$= \binom{n-1}{k-1} p^k (1-p)^{n-k}, n = k, k+1, \ldots$$

This is the probability function for the negative binomial variable Y.

Example

If I throw an unbiased die, find the probability of the third six appearing on the tenth throw.

Solution

We can model the situation with the negative binomial distribution, $n = 10$, $k = 3$ and $p = \dfrac{1}{6}$

$$\Rightarrow P(\text{3rd 6 on 10th throw}) = \binom{10-1}{3-1} \left(\tfrac{1}{6}\right)^3 \left(\tfrac{5}{6}\right)^7$$

$$= \binom{9}{2} \times \dfrac{5^7}{6^{10}} = 0.0465 \quad \text{(3 sig. figs.)}$$

Mean and variance

In fact, we can look at the random variable Y as being the sum of k different random variables $X_1, X_2, \ldots X_k$. X_1 is the number of trials for the first success. X_2 is the subsequent number of trials for the second success, and so on. These k variables each have the same distribution – a geometric distribution with probability p which we can call X.

$$
\begin{aligned}
E(Y) = E(X_1 + X_2 + \ldots + X_k) &= E(X_1) + E(X_2) + \ldots + E(X_k) \\
&= E(X) + E(X) + \ldots + E(X) \\
&= kE(X) \\
&= \dfrac{k}{p}
\end{aligned}
$$

since $\quad E(X) = \dfrac{1}{p}$

Similarly, $\text{Var}(Y) = k\,\text{Var}(X) = \dfrac{k(1-p)}{p^2}$

This derivation is not required in the syllabus: in fact you are given the probability function and the mean and the variance in the formula sheet. The mean and variance for most of the other distributions you have studied are also given.

You should now try Exercises 8–10 at the end of this section.

Exponential distribution

The binomial and Poisson distributions ask a similar kind of question – how many successes or events will I get in a certain number of trials or a certain amount of time?

Figure 1.1

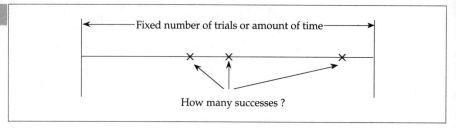

The difference between them lies in the fact that for the binomial distribution, there are only a small number of fixed points at which a success can occur (these are the trials). For the Poisson distribution, there are an infinite number of these points at which something significant can happen (or at least so many that we can look at the points as being continuous. This is when we use the Poisson as an approximation to the binomial.).

Related to the binomial is the geometric distribution. This asks – in a binomial situation, how long will I wait for the first success? The Poisson distribution has a similar partner, the exponential distribution, which we shall look at now. It asks much the same question – in a Poisson situation, how long will I wait for the first event? Equivalently, since the events are independent, the question could be – how long between successive events?

Figure 1.2

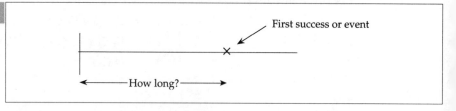

Because the length could be anything, the random variable, Y say, defined by the length of time up to the first event is *continuous*. The other three variables were all *discrete*. This means that we have to use integration instead of summation, and define Y in terms of a continuous probability density function (PDF).

To find this probability density function, $f(x)$, we shall first of all derive the cumulative distribution function, $F(x)$. We can then use the relation

$$f(x) = \frac{dF(x)}{dx}$$

We start by looking at the Poisson distribution with parameter λ. If we call the random variable X,

$$P(X = r) = \frac{e^{-\lambda}\lambda^r}{r!}$$

and in particular $P(X = 0) = e^{-\lambda}$.

We now want to find the probability of at least one Poisson event in x units. Since λ is the number we expect in one unit, we expect λx in x units.

$$\Rightarrow P(X \geq 1 \text{ when we expect } \lambda x) \quad = 1 - P(X = 0)$$
$$= 1 - e^{-\lambda x}$$

Turning now to the random variable Y, which is defined to be the length of time up to the first event (or the time between successive events),

$$P(Y \leq x) \quad = P(\text{at least 1 Poisson event in } x)$$
$$= 1 - e^{-\lambda x}$$

(Note that since Y is continuous, $P(Y \leq x)$ is the same as $P(Y < x)$.)

But this is the definition of the cumulative distribution function, $F(x)$, i.e.

$$F(x) \quad = 1 - e^{-\lambda x}, \ x \geq 0$$
$$\Rightarrow f(x) \quad = \frac{dF(x)}{dx} = \frac{d(1 - e^{-\lambda x})}{dx}$$
$$= \lambda e^{-\lambda x}$$

We can summarise this

> If the random variable X has a Poisson distribution with parameter λ,
>
> then the associated random variable Y with probability density function
>
> $$f(x) = \lambda e^{-\lambda x} \qquad x \geq 0$$
> $$= 0 \qquad x < 0$$
>
> has an exponential distribution with parameter λ.

Mean and variance

The derivation of these is not required in your syllabus, but they are not difficult.

$$E(Y) = \int_0^\infty x f(x) dx \ = \overset{\text{by parts}}{\cdots} = \frac{1}{\lambda}$$

Using $E(Y^2)$ (integrating by parts twice)

and $\quad Var(Y) = E(Y^2) - [E(Y)]^2$,

we find $Var(Y) = \dfrac{1}{\lambda^2}$

These, together with the PDF, are given in the *Formula Book*

Here are some examples using this distribution.

Example   During office hours, telephone calls to a single telephone in an office come in at an average rate of 20 calls per hour. Assuming that a Poisson distribution is relevant, write down the probability function of X, the number of telephone calls arriving in each five-minute period.

Find, to three decimal places, the probability that there will be (a) less than two calls, (b) more than three calls in a five-minute period.

Given that T is the time in minutes between consecutive calls, show that

$$P(0 \leq T \leq t) = 1 - e^{-t/3}$$

The person answering the telephone wishes to leave the office for five minutes. Find, to two decimal places, the probability that, if she leaves immediately after a call, she will return before the next call.

[ULEAC 1984]

Solution   If there are an average of 20 calls per 60 mins, there will be $\frac{20}{12}$ per 5 minutes,

i.e. a Poisson distribution with $\lambda = \frac{5}{3}$

$$\Rightarrow P(X = r) = \frac{e^{-\frac{5}{3}} \left(\frac{5}{3}\right)^r}{r!}, \quad r = 0, 1, 2, \ldots$$

(a) $P(X < 2) = P(X = 0 \text{ or } X = 1)$

$$= e^{-\frac{5}{3}} \left[1 + \frac{5}{3}\right] = 0.504 \quad (3 \text{ d.p.})$$

(b) $P(X > 3) = 1 - P(X = 0, 1, 2 \text{ or } 3)$

$$= 1 - e^{-\frac{5}{3}} \left[1 + \frac{5}{3} + \frac{\left(\frac{5}{3}\right)^2}{2!} + \frac{\left(\frac{5}{3}\right)^3}{3!}\right]$$

$$= 0.088$$

$$p(0 \leq T \leq t) = P(\text{at least one call in } t \text{ mins})$$

In t mins, with one call every three mins, expect $\frac{t}{3}$ calls

$$\Rightarrow P(\text{at least one call}) = 1 - P(\text{none})$$

$$= 1 - e^{-\frac{t}{3}}$$

with $\quad t = 5$, we want $P(T > 5) \;=\; 1 - P(0 \le T \le 5)$

$$= 1 - \left(1 - e^{-\frac{5}{3}}\right)$$

$$= e^{-\frac{5}{3}} \;=\; 0.19 \;\; (2 \text{ d.p.})$$

At least

Note from the last part the probability that the exponential variable is more than a certain value, x say:

$$
\begin{aligned}
P(Y > x) \;&=\; 1 - P(Y \le x) \\
&=\; 1 - F(x) \\
&=\; 1 - \left[1 - e^{-\lambda x}\right] \\
&=\; e^{-\lambda x}
\end{aligned}
$$

$$\Rightarrow \;\; P(y > x) \;=\; e^{-\lambda x}$$

Here are a further two examples.

Example

The continuous random variable X has the exponential distribution whose probability density function is given by

$$f(x) \;=\; \lambda e^{-\lambda x}, \, x \ge 0$$
$$f(x) \;=\; 0, \, \text{otherwise}$$

where λ is a positive constant.

Television sets are hired out by a rental company. The time in months, X, between major repairs has the above exponential distribution with $\lambda = 0.05$. Find, to three significant figures, the probability that a television set hired out by the company will not require a major repair for at least a two-year period.

Find also the median value of X.

The company agrees to replace any set for which the time between major repairs is less than M months. Given that the company does not want to have to replace more than one set in five, find M.

[ULEAC 1986]

Solution

We need $P(X > 24)$ (Note that there has to be agreement in units.)

From the formula above,

$$P(X > 24) = e^{-24 \times 0.05} = 0.301 \;\; (3 \text{ sig.figs.})$$

The median is given from the cumulative distribution function F(x) by

$$F(m) = \frac{1}{2}$$

The cumulative distribution function (CDF) for an exponential distribution is

$$F(x) = P(X < x) = 1 - e^{-\lambda x}$$

We need $F(m) = \frac{1}{2} \Rightarrow 1 - e^{-\lambda m} = \frac{1}{2}$

$$\Rightarrow \quad e^{-\lambda m} = \frac{1}{2}$$

Taking ln's, $\ln(e^{-\lambda m}) = \ln\frac{1}{2}$

$$\Rightarrow \quad -\lambda m = \ln\frac{1}{2}$$

$$\Rightarrow \quad \lambda m = \ln 2, \text{ since } \ln\frac{1}{2} = -\ln 2$$

$$\Rightarrow \quad m = \frac{\ln 2}{\lambda} = \frac{0.693}{0.05} = 13.9 \text{ months } (3 \text{ sig.figs.})$$

For the last part, we need

$$P(X < M) \leq 0.2$$
$$\Rightarrow 1 - e^{-\lambda M} \leq 0.2$$
$$e^{-M} \geq 0.8$$

$$\Rightarrow M \leq \frac{-\ln 0.8}{\lambda} = 4.46$$

Since M is an integer, M = 4.

Example

On a certain production line that operates continuously for 24 hours a day, seven days a week, breakdowns occur at random at a rate of 0.5 per week.

(a) Find the probability that there is no breakdown in the next week.

A service engineer is employed to repair such breakdowns. Immediately after the production line has restarted, following a breakdown, the engineer takes a two-week holiday.

(b) Determine the expected time that elapses before the next breakdown occurs.

(c) Find the probability that the next breakdown occurs before the engineer has returned from his holiday.

[ULEAC 1996]

| **Solution** | We have a Poisson distribution with $\lambda = 0.5$. |

(a) $P(\text{none}) = e^{-\lambda} = e^{-0.5} = 0.607$ (3 sig.figs.)

(b) The time before the next breakdown has an exponential distribution
with $\lambda = 0.5$. The mean is $\dfrac{1}{\lambda} = \dfrac{1}{0.5} = 2$ weeks (expected time)

(c) $P(X < 2) = 1 - e^{-2 \times 0.5} = 1 - e^{-1}$

$$= 0.632$$

You should now try Exercises 11–15.

EXERCISES

1 An unfair coin is such that the probability of obtaining a head when it
is tossed is 0.4. The coin is tossed repeatedly until the first head is
obtained. Assuming that each toss is independent of all other tosses,
find the probability that the first head is obtained on the third toss.

State the expected number of tosses in order to obtain the first head.

[UCLES 1995]

2 I sit in a café and watch people go by. For each person that goes by, the
probability that I know their name is 0.04. Assuming independence,
find the probability that the fifth person who goes by is the first person
whose name I know, giving your answer correct to three decimal
places.

[UCLES 1995]

3 For the purpose of sampling, a computer generates a series of random
numbers, each of which is an integer in the range 1 to 1000 inclusive.
Each such integer is equally likely to be generated, independently of
other integers in the series. A number generated is 'acceptable' if it lies
in the range 1 to 278 inclusive. The first 'acceptable' number is the Rth
number generated.

(i) State the distribution of R.

(ii) Calculate the probability that $R = 3$.

(iii) Find the mean and variance of R.

[UCLES 1995]

4 (i)   A fair coin is tossed until a head has been obtained. Find the probability that exactly five tosses are required.

(ii)   A fair coin is tossed until both a head and a tail have been obtained. Find the probability that exactly five tosses are required.

[UCLES 1996]

5 On a production line 12% of completed items are faulty. Each completed item is tested. The number of items that have been tested when the first faulty item is found is X. Stating a necessary assumption, suggest an appropriate model for the distribution of X.

Using your model, find

(i) $P(X \geq 3)$

(ii) $E(X)$.

[UCLES 1996]

6 State the conditions which give rise to a geometric distribution whose probability function is $P(X = r) = (1 - p)^{r-1} p$, $r = 1, 2, 3 \dots$ where $0 < p < 1$.

Prove that $P(X \leq r) = 1 - (1 - p)^r$.

Hence prove that, for any two positive integers s and t,

$P(X > s + t \mid X > s) = P(X > t)$,

and explain in words the meaning of this result.

During the winter in Glen Shee, the probability that snow will fall on any given day is 0.1. Taking November 1st as the first day of winter and assuming independence from day to day, find, to two significant figures, the probability that the first snow of winter will fall in Glen Shee on the last day of November (30th).

Given that no snow has fallen at Glen Shee during the whole of November, a man decides that he can wait no longer to book his skiing holiday. He decides to book for the earliest date for which the probability that snow will have fallen on or before that date is at least 0.9. Find the date of his booking.

[ULEAC 1985]

7 The discrete random variable X has a geometric distribution defined by

$$P(X = r) = p(1 - p)^{r-1}, \ r = 1, 2, 3, \dots$$

Show that $E(X) = \dfrac{1}{p}$.

Each of n players, where $n > 2$, tosses a fair coin. If the result of any player's toss is different from that of all the remaining players, then that player wins the game. Otherwise all the players toss again until one player wins. Given that X is the number of tosses each player makes, up to and including the one on which the game is won, find $P(X = r)$ in terms of r and n.

Show that $E(X) = \dfrac{2^{n-1}}{n}$.

Given that $n = 7$, find the least number k such that $P(X \le k) > 0.5$.

[UCLES 1988]

8 Alice will attempt to speak on a 'phone-in' programme on her local radio station once each day until she has been allowed to speak three times. Assume that there is a probability of 0.1 that she will be allowed to speak on any given day, independent of all the other days. Let X be the number of days she phones in.

(a) Using an appropriate probability distribution to model the situation, write down the probability function for X.

(b) Calculate the probability that $X = 21$.

(c) Comment on whether the independence assumption made above is likely to be true in practice.

[ULEAC 1996]

9 Player A is having a series of games of tennis with Player B. Player B is in fact better than Player A and the probability that B wins any particular set is 0.7. Player A is determined that she will not stop playing until she has won three sets. Letting X be the random variable – the number of sets played – and assuming independence of results, find

(i) $P(X = 7)$.

(ii) The mean and variance of X.

10 (a) A sequence of independent trials is performed, each having probability p of success and $q = 1 - p$ of failure. The nth success occurs on the Xth trial.

Given that

$$P(X = x) = \frac{(x-1)!}{(n-1)!\,(x-n)!}\, p^n q^{x-n} \quad (x = n, n+1, n+2, \dots).$$

Show that, for $x \ge n + 1$,

$$\frac{P(X = x)}{P(X = x - 1)} = \frac{(x-1)q}{x-n}$$

123

Deduce that $P(X = x) > P(X = x - 1)$ as long as

$$x < \frac{n - q}{p}$$

(b) In order to promote sales, a chewing gum manufacturer introduces gift vouchers randomly into 12% of the packets. To quality for a gift, six of these vouchers have to be collected.

A student wishing to qualify for a gift goes to a shop and buys packets of the chewing gum one at a time, opening them to see whether or not they contain a voucher. Calculate the most likely number of packets that she must buy in order to collect her six vouchers.

[Oxford 1992]

11 An archer shoots arrows at a target. The distance X cm from the centre of the target at which an arrow strikes the target has probability density function, f, defined by

$$f(x) = \frac{1}{10} e^{-\frac{x}{10}}, \quad x > 0$$

$$f(x) = 0, \qquad \text{otherwise}$$

An arrow scores eight points if $X \le 2$, five points if $2 < X \le 5$, one point if $5 < X \le 15$ and no points otherwise. Find, to three decimal places, the expected score when one arrow is shot at the target.

[ULEAC 1987]

12 Customers arrive at a Post Office queue at random at a rate of 7.2 customers per five minutes.

(a) Calculate the probability that the time interval between the first two arrivals is less than 30 seconds.

(b) Calculate the probability that the time interval between the second and third arrivals is between one and two minutes.

[ULEAC 1996]

13 During working hours an office switchboard receives telephone calls at random at an average rate of one call every 40 seconds.

The probability density function of the time, in minutes, between consecutive calls can be modelled using the exponential distribution. Write down the probability density function of the time, in minutes, between consecutive calls received by the above switchboard. Hence find the cumulative distribution function of the time, in minutes, between consecutive calls.

Given that a call occurs at 11.30 am precisely, find, to three decimal places, the probability that the next call will occur between 11.32 am and 11.33 am.

[ULEAC 1992]

14 A random variable X has the probability density function f given by

$$f(x) = ce^{-2x} \quad x > 0$$

$$f(x) = 0, \qquad \text{otherwise.}$$

Find the value of c.

Find the cumulative distribution function of X.

Hence, or otherwise, show that, for positive t and k,

$$P(X > t + k \mid X > k) = P(X > t).$$

Given that X is the lifetime in years of a particular type of indicator lamp that is alight continuously, explain in words the meaning of the above result.

Given that two such lamps, A and B, have already been alight for three months and four months respectively, find the probability that both will still be alight in three months time.

[ULEAC 1986]

15 A major road construction project is underway. In the site supervisor's office, there is an average of two telephone calls every five minutes. Stating any assumptions you make, write down the probability that in a period of t minutes there is

(a) no telephone call

(b) at least one telephone call.

Presenting a carefully reasoned argument, give the cumulative distribution function, $F(t)$, for the length of time between telephone calls. Hence establish that the probability density function, $f(t)$, is

$$f(t) = 0.4e^{-0.4t}; \quad t > 0$$

Calculate

(c) the mean time between calls

(d) the median time between calls.

(e) Given that the supervisor has had no call in the last three minutes, what is the probability that she could leave the office for five minutes without missing a call?

[Oxford 1988]

125

SUMMARY   When you have finished this section you should

- be familiar with the probability function for the geometric distribution

- know its mean and variance

- know the conditions for it to be appropriate to use it as a model in a given situation

- be familiar with the probability function for the negative binomial

- know its mean and variance

- know that the conditions for it to be an appropriate model are the same as for the binomial and geometric distributions

- be familiar with the definition of the exponential distribution and when it is appropriate to use it as a model

- be able to derive $F(x)$, the cumulative distribution function

- from $F(x)$, be able to derive $f(x)$, the probability density function

- know its mean and variance.

8

Probability generating functions

INTRODUCTION In this section we shall look at a method for condensing all the information contained in the probability function into a single function and how this single function can then be used.

By the end of this section you should be able to:

● use probability generating functions

● derive probability generating functions for the geometric, Poisson and binomial distributions

● find the mean and variance for the geometric, Poisson and binomial distributions.

From your work on the binomial distribution you know that the general formula for a particular probability is

$$P(r \text{ successes out of } n \text{ trials}) = {}^nC_r \, p^r q^{n-r}$$

With the help of this formula we can find the probabilities for all the possible number of successes. (The notation ${}^nC_r$ means the same as $\binom{n}{r}$; the syllabus requires that you are familiar with both forms.) For example, if X has a binomial distribution with parameters $n = 3$ and $p = \frac{1}{3}$, then

$$
\begin{aligned}
P(X = 0) &= {}^3C_0 \left(\tfrac{1}{3}\right)^0 \left(\tfrac{2}{3}\right)^3 = \left(\tfrac{2}{3}\right)^3 \\
P(X = 1) &= {}^3C_1 \left(\tfrac{1}{3}\right)^1 \left(\tfrac{2}{3}\right)^2 = 3\left(\tfrac{1}{3}\right)\left(\tfrac{2}{3}\right)^2 \\
P(X = 2) &= {}^3C_2 \left(\tfrac{1}{3}\right)^2 \left(\tfrac{2}{3}\right)^1 = 3\left(\tfrac{1}{3}\right)^2 \left(\tfrac{2}{3}\right) \\
P(X = 3) &= {}^3C_3 \left(\tfrac{1}{3}\right)^3 \left(\tfrac{2}{3}\right)^0 = \left(\tfrac{1}{3}\right)^3
\end{aligned}
$$

Somebody then discovered an interesting connection – if you expand $\left(\frac{2}{3} + \frac{1}{3}t\right)^3$ as a series, it becomes

$$\left(\tfrac{2}{3} + \tfrac{1}{3}t\right)^3 = \left(\tfrac{2}{3}\right)^3 t^0 + 3\left(\tfrac{2}{3}\right)^2 \left(\tfrac{1}{3}\right)t + 3\left(\tfrac{2}{3}\right)\left(\tfrac{1}{3}\right)^2 t^2 + \left(\tfrac{1}{3}\right)^3 t^3$$

The coefficients of the powers of t are exactly the probabilities that were found above. The function

$G(t) = \left(\frac{2}{3} + \frac{1}{3}t\right)^3$ is called a *probability generating function*. It turns out that if we can find this function for a particular probability distribution, we can derive some important quantities relating to the distribution, including the mean and variance.

Definition

If X is a random variable which can only take the values 0, 1, 2, ... then the probability generating function (hereafter PGF) for X is defined as

$$G(t) = p_0 t^0 + p_1 t^1 + p_2 t^2 + \dots$$

where p_i is $P(X = i)$.

For example, if X has probability distribution

X_i	0	1	2	3
p_i	$\frac{1}{4}$	$\frac{1}{3}$	$\frac{1}{4}$	$\frac{1}{6}$

then X has PGF $G(t) = \frac{1}{4}t^0 + \frac{1}{3}t^1 + \frac{1}{4}t^2 + \frac{1}{6}t^3$

Mean

If the probability distribution for X is given by

X_i	0	1	2	3	4	...
p_i	p_0	p_1	p_2	p_3	p_4	...

we know that we can find the mean, or expected value for X, by multiplying each value by its corresponding probability and adding:

$$E(X) = \sum_i X_i p_i = 0 \times p_0 + 1 \times p_1 + 2 \times p_2 + 3 \times p_3 + \dots$$
$$= p_1 + 2p_2 + 3p_3 + \dots$$

Turning to our PGF for X, we have

$$G(t) = p_0 + p_1 t + p_2 t^2 + p_3 t^3 + \dots$$

Differentiating this with respect to t gives

$$G'(t) = p_1 + 2p_2 t^1 + 3p_3 t^2 + \dots$$

and putting $t = 1$,

$$G'(1) = p_1 + 2p_2 + 3p_3 + \dots$$

which is the same as our expression for $E(X)$, i.e.

> If the random variable X has PGF $G(t)$, then $E(X) = G'(1)$

Variance

We can also show that $Var(X) = G''(1) + G'(1) - [G'(1)]^2$, where $G''(t)$ means $G(t)$ differentiated twice with respect to t. The proof of this is at the end of this section.

Standard distributions

If the probability distribution has no regularity (cannot be put into a formula) or symmetry, there is little advantage to be gained in finding the PGF in most cases. The PGF really comes into its own with distributions where the probabilities can be summed up in a single formula. This includes all the discrete distributions that we have studied: the binomial, Poisson, geometric etc. In these cases, the PGF also simplifies into a single formula whose expansion gives the probability of all the possible outcomes. The technique of differentiating and substituting $t = 1$ then becomes a powerful and useful method for finding the mean and variance. We'll look at these standard distributions in turn. The general method is to form the PGF

$$G(t) = p_0 + p_1 t + p_2 t^2 + p_3 t^3 + \ldots$$

where p_i is given by the formula $P(X = i)$ for the particular distribution. Then we try and find some way of simplifying $G(t)$ so that it can be expressed as a single formula.

We'll start with the geometric distribution.

Geometric distribution

The geometric distribution has probability function

$$P(X = r) = p(1 - p)^{r-1}; r = 1, 2, \ldots$$

X cannot take the value of zero, i.e. $P(X = 0) = p_0 = 0$

$$P(X = 1) = p_1 = p(1-p)^0 = p \qquad P(X = 2) = p_2 = p(1-p)^1 = pq$$
$$P(X = 3) = p_3 = p(1-p)^2 = pq^2 \quad P(X = 3) = p_3 = p(1-p)^3 = pq^3, \ldots \text{ etc.}$$

where $q = 1 - p$

Substituting these into $G(t) = p_0 + p_1 t + p_2 t^2 + p_3 t^3 + \ldots$ gives

$$G(t) = pt + pqt^2 + pq^2 t^3 + pq^3 t^4 + \ldots = pt[1 + qt + q^2 t^2 + q^3 t^3 + \ldots]$$

The bracket is the same expansion as

$$\frac{1}{1-x} = 1 + x + x^2 + x^3 + \dots$$

with qt instead of x. This means that the PGF has the compact form

$$G(t) = \frac{pt}{1 - qt}, \text{ where } q = 1 - p$$

Mean and variance

From this we can find the mean and variance by differentiating with respect to t

$$G'(t) = \frac{(1 - qt)p - pt(-q)}{(1 - qt)^2} = \frac{p}{(1 - qt)^2} = p(1 - qt)^{-2}$$

Differentiating again

$$G''(t) = 2pq(1 - qt)^{-3}$$

Substituting $t = 1$

Then $E(X) = G'(1) = p(1 - q)^{-2} = p \times p^{-2}$ since $1 - q = p$

$$= \frac{1}{p}$$

$$\text{Var}(X) = G''(1) + G'(1) - [G'(1)]^2$$

$$= \frac{2pq}{p^3} + \frac{1}{p} - \frac{1}{p^2} = \frac{2q + p - 1}{p^2} = \frac{q}{p^2}$$

Knowledge of the derivation of the mean and variance of the geometric (and Poisson and binomial) distribution is included in the syllabus, so you will need to be able to reproduce them.

Poisson distribution

The Poisson distribution with parameter λ is written as $X \sim \text{Po}(\lambda)$ and has probability distribution

$$P(X = r) = \frac{e^{-\lambda}\lambda^r}{r!}$$

This gives $p_0 = P(X = 0) = \dfrac{e^{-\lambda}\lambda^0}{0!} = e^{-\lambda}; p_1 = P(X = 1) = \dfrac{e^{-\lambda}\lambda^1}{1!}$ etc.

and the PGF then has the form

$$G(t) = e^{-\lambda}t^0 + \frac{e^{-\lambda}\lambda}{1!}t + \frac{e^{-\lambda}\lambda^2}{2!}t^2 + \frac{e^{-\lambda}\lambda^3}{3!}t^3 + \dots$$

$$= e^{-\lambda}\left[1 + \frac{(\lambda t)^1}{1!} + \frac{(\lambda t)^2}{2!} + \frac{(\lambda t)^3}{3!} + \dots\right] \longleftarrow \quad \begin{array}{l}\text{The bracket is just}\\ \text{the expansion of } e^{\lambda t}\end{array}$$

$$G(t) = e^{-\lambda}\,(e^{\lambda t}) = e^{\lambda t - \lambda} = e^{\lambda(t-1)}$$

i.e.

$$G(t) = e^{\lambda(t-1)}$$

Mean and variance

Differentiating the above PGF with respect to t (remembering that λ is constant),

$$G'(t) = \lambda e^{\lambda(t-1)}$$
$$G''(t) = \lambda^2 e^{\lambda(t-1)}$$

This gives

$$E(X) = G'(1) = \lambda e^0 = \lambda$$

$$\mathrm{Var}(X) = G''(1) + G'(1) - \left[G'(1)\right]^2$$
$$= \lambda^2 + \lambda - \lambda^2 = \lambda$$

Binomial distribution

A binomial random variable X with parameters n and p is written as $X \sim B(n,p)$ and has probability distribution

$$P(X = r) = {}^nC_r\, p^r q^{n-r}$$

where $q = 1 - p$

$$p_0 = P(x = 0) = {}^nC_0\, p^0 q^{n-0} = q^n \; ; \; p_1 = P(x = 1) = {}^nC_1\, p^1 q^{n-1} \quad \text{etc.}$$

$$G(t) = q^n t^0 + \binom{n}{1} q^{n-1} pt + \binom{n}{2} q^{n-2} p^2 t^2 + \binom{n}{3} q^{n-3} p^3 t^3 + \dots$$

$$\dots + \binom{n}{n-1} qp^{n-1} t^{n-1} + p^n t^n$$

$$= q^n + \binom{n}{1} q^{n-1}(pt) + \binom{n}{2} q^{n-2}(pt)^2 + \dots + (pt)^n$$

$$= (q + pt)^n$$

i.e.

$$G(t) = (q + pt)^n$$

Differentiating $G(t)$ with respect to t and remembering that n, p and q are constant

$$G'(t) = np(q + pt)^{n-1}$$
$$G''(t) = n(n-1)p^2(q + pt)^{n-2}$$

giving $E(X) = G'(1)$ $= np(q + p) = np$

$\quad\quad\quad$ $Var(X)$ $= G''(1) + G'(1) - \left(G'(1)\right)^2$

$\quad\quad\quad\quad\quad\quad\quad$ $= n(n-1)p^2(p + q)^{n-2} + np - (np)^2$

$\quad\quad\quad\quad\quad\quad\quad$ $= n(n-1)p^2 + np - n^2p^2$

$\quad\quad\quad\quad\quad\quad\quad$ $= n^2p^2 - np^2 + np - n^2p^2$

$\quad\quad\quad\quad\quad\quad\quad$ $= np - np^2 = np(1-p) = npq$

This completes the derivation of the mean and variance for the geometric, Poisson and binomial distributions. Make sure you can reproduce them: they are all specifically mentioned in the syllabus and any of the proofs could be asked for in your exam.

Sums of distributions

Suppose we have the random variables X and Y with corresponding PGFs $G(t)$ and $H(t)$. For simplicity here, we'll suppose that

$$G(t) = p_0 + p_1 t^1 + p^2 t^2 + \dots \quad \text{and}$$
$$H(t) = q_0 + q_1 t^1 + q^2 t^2 + \dots$$

where p_i, q_i are the respective probabilities that X and Y take the value i.

Now the probability that $X + Y$ has the value of 0,

$\quad\quad\quad\quad$ $P(X + Y = 0)$ $= P(X = 0 \text{ and } Y = 0)$

$\quad\quad\quad\quad\quad\quad\quad\quad\quad$ $= p_0 q_0$

and $\quad\quad\quad$ $P(X + Y = 1)$ $= P(X = 0 \text{ and } Y = 1) + P(X = 1 \text{ and } Y = 0)$

$\quad\quad\quad\quad\quad\quad\quad\quad\quad$ $= p_0 q_1 + p_1 q_0$

Similarly $\quad$ $P(X + Y = 2)$ $= p_0 q_2 + p_1 q_1 + p_2 q_0$

and $\quad\quad\quad$ $P(X + Y = 3)$ $= p_0 q_3 + p_1 q_2 + p_2 q_1 + p_3 q_0 \quad$ etc.

If we now take the PGFs for X and Y, and multiply to give the first few terms, we get

$\quad\quad$ $G(t) H(t)$ $= (p_0 + p_1 t + p_2 t^2 + p_3 t^3 + \dots)(q_0 + q_1 t + q_2 t^2 + q_3 t^3 + \dots)$

$\quad\quad\quad\quad\quad$ $= (p_0 q_0)t^0$

$\quad\quad\quad\quad\quad$ $+ (p_1 q_0 + p_0 q_1)t$

$\quad\quad\quad\quad\quad$ $+ (p_2 q_0 + p_1 q_1 + p_0 q_2)t^2$

$\quad\quad\quad\quad\quad$ $+ (p_3 q_0 + p_2 q_1 + p_1 q_2 + p_0 q_3)t^3$

$\quad\quad\quad\quad\quad$ $+ \dots$ etc.

The coefficients in the brackets are the same as the probabilities of the different values for $X + Y$ that we found above. We can write

$$G(t) H(t) = P(X + Y = 0)t^0 + P(X + Y = 1)t^1 + P(X + Y = 2)t^2 + \dots$$

i.e. $\quad$ $G(t) H(t)$ is the PGF of $X + Y$.

If X_1 and X_2 are two independent random variables with PGFs $G_1(t)$ and $G_2(t)$ respectively, $X_1 + X_2$ has the PGF

$$G_1(t)\, G_2(t)$$

Example

If X has PGF $G(t) = \frac{1}{2} + \frac{1}{3}t + \frac{1}{6}t^2$

and Y has PGF $H(t) = \frac{1}{2}t + \frac{1}{2}t^2$, find the probability that $X + Y$ has the value of 3.

Solution

$X + Y$ has PGF $G(t)\, H(t) = \left(\frac{1}{2} + \frac{1}{3}t + \frac{1}{6}t^2\right)\left(\frac{1}{2}t + \frac{1}{2}t^2\right)$.

We want $P(X + Y = 3)$, i.e. we want the coefficient of t^3 in the expansion of $G(t)\, H(t)$. This can only come from multiplying terms in t with terms in t^2.

The term in t^3 is $\quad \frac{1}{3}t \times \frac{1}{2}t^2 + \frac{1}{6}t^2 \times \frac{1}{2}t$

$$= \frac{1}{6}t^3 + \frac{1}{12}t^3 = \frac{1}{4}t^3$$

The coefficient here is $\frac{1}{4}$, and so $P(X + Y = 3) = \frac{1}{4}$.

Example

If Y has the PGF given above, find the probability that the sum of three successive values for Y is 4.

Solution

The PGF for Y is $H(t) = \frac{1}{2}t + \frac{1}{2}t^2 = \frac{1}{2}t(1 + t)$.

Denoting the three successive values for Y by Y_1, Y_2 and Y_3, we want $P(Y_1 + Y_2 + Y_3 = 4)$.

But the PGF of $Y_1 + Y_2 + Y_3$ is $[H(t)]^3$ since they each have PGF $H(t)$. This is $\left[\frac{1}{2}t(1 + t)\right]^3 = \frac{1}{8}t^3(1 + t)^3$. With t^3 outside the bracket, to find the overall coefficient of t^4, we need the coefficient of t when the bracket is expanded. This is 3, and so the term in t^4 is $\frac{1}{8}t^3 \times 3t = \frac{3}{8}t^4$. This means that

$$P(Y_1 + Y_2 + Y_3 = 4) = \frac{3}{8}.$$

Further properties

If X has PGF

$$G(t) = p_0 + p_1 t + p_2 t^2 + \ldots$$

then

$$G(1) = p_0 + p_1 + p_2 + \ldots = \sum_i p_i = 1$$

Also substituting $t = -1$ into $G(t)$ gives

$$
\begin{aligned}
G(-1) &= p_0 - p_1 + p_2 - p_3 + \ldots \\
&= (p_0 + p_2 + p_4 + \ldots) - (p_1 + p_3 + p_5 + \ldots) \\
&= \Sigma\, P(\text{evens}) - \Sigma\, P(\text{odds})
\end{aligned}
$$

> For a PGF $G(t)$, we have $G(1) = 1$ and $G(-1) = \Sigma\, P(\text{evens}) - \Sigma\, P(\text{odds})$

Here are some examples which use these ideas. The later ones are probably more complicated than those you are likely to encounter in your exam.

Example

The PGF of a discrete r.v. X is $(az + 1 - a)^n$, where a is a constant $(0 \le a \le 1)$ and n is a positive integer. Prove that $E(X) = an$ and find the variance of X.

[UCLES, 1982]

Solution

We use $E(X) = G'(1)$, where

$$G(z) = (az + 1 - a)^n$$

Differentiating with respect to z,

$$G'(z) = an(az + 1 - a)^{n-1}$$

and so $E(X) = G'(1) = an(a + 1 - a)^{n-1} = an$

Differentiating $G'(z)$ gives $G''(z) = a^2 n(n-1)(az + 1 - a)^{n-2}$

$$\Rightarrow \qquad G''(1) = a^2 n(n-1)$$

Using $\mathrm{Var}(X) = G''(1) + G'(1) - \left[G'(1)\right]^2$

gives

$$
\begin{aligned}
\mathrm{Var}(X) &= a^2 n(n-1) + an - a^2 n^2 \\
&= a^2 n^2 - a^2 n + an - a^2 n^2 \\
&= an - a^2 n \\
&= an(1 - a)
\end{aligned}
$$

Example

An electronic device has three windows in which any of the digits 1, 2 or 3 can be displayed independently when a button is pressed. For each of the three windows, the probability that a 1 appears is $\frac{1}{8}$, the probability that a 2 appears is $\frac{5}{8}$ and the probability that a 3 appears is $\frac{1}{4}$.

(i) Find the probability generating function, $G(t)$, for the **total** of the three numbers displayed.

(ii) Evaluate $G(-1)$. Hence find the probability that the total of the three numbers displayed is even.

[UCLES Specimen paper S4]

Solution

(i) The PGF for each of the windows is

$$G(t) = \tfrac{1}{8}t + \tfrac{5}{8}t^2 + \tfrac{1}{4}t^3$$

The PGF for the total of the three numbers displayed (assuming independence) is

$$G(t) \quad = \left[G(t)\right]^3 = \left[\tfrac{1}{8}t + \tfrac{5}{8}t^2 + \tfrac{1}{4}t^3\right]^3$$

(ii) $G(-1) = \left(-\tfrac{1}{8} + \tfrac{5}{8} - \tfrac{1}{4}\right)^3 = \tfrac{1}{64}$

This is $\Sigma P(\text{evens}) - \Sigma P(\text{odds})$, so

$$\Sigma P(\text{evens}) - \Sigma P(\text{odds}) = \tfrac{1}{64} \qquad \qquad \dots \text{①}$$

but $\Sigma P(\text{evens}) + \Sigma P(\text{odds}) = 1 \qquad \qquad \dots \text{②}$

$\Rightarrow \quad 2\Sigma P(\text{evens}) = \tfrac{65}{64} \Rightarrow \Sigma P(\text{evens}) = \tfrac{65}{128}$

Example

The random variable X has a Poisson distribution with mean λ.

(i) Show that the probability generating function for X is

$$G(t) = \exp\{\lambda(t - 1)\}$$

Given that $E[X(X - 1) \dots (X - k + 1)] = G^{(k)}(1)$ for $k \geq 1$,

where $G^{(k)}(t)$ is the kth derivative of $G(t)$ with respect to t, prove that $\text{Var}(X) = \lambda$.

(ii) Prove that $E(X^3) = \lambda^3 + 3\lambda^2 + \lambda$.

[Oxford and Cambridge, 1994]

Solution

If $\quad X \sim \text{Po}(\lambda) \implies P(X = r) = \dfrac{e^{-\lambda}\lambda^r}{r!}$

$$P(X = 0) \quad = e^{-\lambda}$$
$$P(X = 1) \quad = e^{-\lambda}\lambda$$
$$P(X = 2) \quad = e^{-\lambda}\dfrac{\lambda^2}{2!}$$
$$P(X = 3) \quad = e^{-\lambda}\dfrac{\lambda^3}{3!}$$

Then $\quad G(t) \quad = (e^{-\lambda}) + (e^{-\lambda}\lambda)t + \left(e^{-\lambda}\dfrac{\lambda^2}{2!}\right)t^2 + \ldots$

$$= e^{-\lambda}\left[1 + (\lambda t) + \dfrac{(\lambda t)^2}{2!} + \dfrac{(\lambda t)^3}{3!} + \ldots\right]$$

$$= e^{-\lambda}e^{\lambda t}$$

$$= e^{\lambda(t-1)} \text{ as required}$$

Putting $\quad k = 1$ into the give expression gives $E(X) = G'(1)$

$$= \left[\lambda e^{\lambda(t-1)}\right]_{t=1}$$

$$= \lambda e^0 = \lambda$$

Putting $\quad k = 2$ into the expression gives $E\big(X(X-1)\big) = G''(1)$

$$\implies \quad E(X^2 - X) = E(X^2) - E(X) = G''(1)$$

Now $\quad G'(t) = \lambda e^{\lambda(t-1)} \implies \quad G'''(t) = \lambda^2 e^{\lambda(t-1)}$

i.e. $\qquad E(X^2) - E(X) = \lambda^2$

But $\qquad E(X) = \lambda \implies E(X^2) = \lambda^2 + \lambda$

$$\text{Var}(X) = E(X^2) - \big(E(X)\big)^2 = (\lambda^2 + \lambda) - (\lambda)^2$$

$$= \lambda$$

Similarly, $G'''(t) = \lambda^3 e^{\lambda(t-1)} \implies \quad G'''(1) = \lambda^3$

Using $\quad E\big(X(X-1)(X-2)\big) = G'''(1)$ gives

$$E(X^3 - 3X^2 + 2X) = \lambda^3$$

$$\implies E(X^3) - 3E(X^2) + 2E(X) = \lambda^3$$

$$\implies E(X^3) - 3(\lambda^2 + \lambda) + 2(\lambda) = \lambda^3$$

i.e. $\quad E(X^3) = \lambda^3 + 3\lambda^2 + \lambda$

Example

The random variable X has a binomial distribution with parameters $n = 6$ and $p = \frac{1}{2}$. Show that the probability generating function of X is $\frac{1}{64}(1 + t)^6$.

Use this generating function to find the mean and variance of X.

The discrete random variable Y, which is independent of X, has the same mean as X and has probability generating function $\frac{t}{a - bt}$. Find the value of each of the constants a and b, and show that Y has a geometric distribution. Calculate $P(X + Y = 3)$.

[UCLES, 1993]

Solution

If $B \sim \text{Bin}(1, \frac{1}{2})$, i.e. $P(B = 0) = \frac{1}{2} = P(B = 1)$, then B has the PGF

$$\frac{1}{2} + \frac{1}{2}t = \frac{1}{2}(1 + t)$$

But X is the sum of six independent values of B.

Using $G_{B_1 + B_2}(t) = G_{B_1}(t)\, G_{B_2}(t)$ repeatedly for the six identical PGFs gives the PGF of X as

$$\left[\frac{1}{2}(1 + t)\right]^6 = \frac{1}{64}(1 + t)^6$$

[An alternative solution would have been to enumerate the probabilities of X taking the values 0 to 6, deducing the PGF and showing that it could be simplified to the given form.]

$$G(t) = \frac{1}{64}(1 + t)^6$$

$$\Rightarrow G'(t) = \frac{6}{64}(1 + t)^5 \quad \text{and} \quad G''(T) = \frac{30}{64}(1 + t)^4$$

$$\text{Using} \quad \text{mean} = E(X) = G'(1)$$

$$\Rightarrow E(X) = \frac{6}{64}(1 + 1)^5 = \frac{6}{64} \times 32 = 3$$

$$\text{Using variance} = G''(1) + G'(1) - \left[G'(1)\right]^2 \text{ gives}$$

$$\text{Var}(X) = \frac{30}{64}(2)^4 + 3 - 9$$

$$= 7\frac{1}{2} + 3 - 9 = 1.5$$

[Since the mean and variance of the binomial are np and npq respectively, we can check that these solutions are correct.]

Let the PGF for Y be $H(t) = \dfrac{t}{a - bt}$

We use the two facts that $H(1) = 1$ and $H'(1) = E(Y)$ to find two simultaneous equations in a and b.

$$H(1) = 1 \quad \Rightarrow \quad \frac{1}{a-b} = 1 \quad \Rightarrow \quad a - b = 1 \qquad \ldots \text{①}$$

$$H'(1) = 3 \text{ (given)} \quad \Rightarrow \quad \left[\frac{(a-bt)\,1 - t(-b)}{a-bt} \right]_{t=1} = 3$$

$$\Rightarrow \quad \frac{a-b+b}{a-b} = 3 \quad \Rightarrow \quad a = 3(a-b) \qquad \ldots \text{②}$$

Putting ① into ② gives $a = 3 \Rightarrow b = 2$

This gives the PGF of Y as $H(t) = \dfrac{t}{3-2t}$

But we need the PGF of a geometric distribution to be of the form $\dfrac{pt}{1-qt}$ where $q = 1 - p$.

Dividing H(t) top and bottom by 3 gives

$$H(t) = \frac{\frac{1}{3}t}{1 - \frac{2}{3}t} \quad \text{which is of the required form with } p = \frac{1}{3}$$

Hence Y has a geometric distribution with $p = \frac{1}{3}$

The PGF of $X + Y$ is $G(t)\,H(t) = \frac{1}{64}(1+t)^6 \times \frac{1}{3}t\left(1 - \frac{2}{3}t\right)^{-1}$

The first few terms of these expressions give

$$G(t)\,H(t) = \frac{t}{192}\left(1 + 6t + 15t^2 + \ldots \right)\left(1 + \frac{2}{3}t + \frac{4}{9}t^2 + \ldots\right)$$

Since we have t outside the brackets we need the coefficient of t^2 when the brackets are multiplied.

This is

$$1 \times \frac{4}{9} + 6 \times \frac{2}{3} + 15 \times 1 = 19\frac{4}{9}$$

Overall, we have $P(X + Y = 3) = \text{coefficient of } t^3$

$$= \frac{1}{192} \times 19\frac{4}{9}$$

$$= \frac{175}{1728} = 0.101 \text{ (3 sig.figs.)}$$

Example	In each round of a quiz a contestant can answer up to three questions. Each correct answer scores one point and allows the contestant to go on to the next question. A wrong answer scores nothing. The contestant is allowed no further question in that round once a wrong answer is given. If all three questions are answered correctly a bonus point of one is scored, making a total score of four for the round. For a certain contestant, A, the probability of giving a correct answer to any question in any round is $\frac{2}{3}$. The random variable X_r is the number of points scored by A *during* the rth round. Write down the probability generating function of X_r and find the mean and variance of X_r.

Write down an expression for the probability generating function of $X_1 + X_2$ and find the probability that A has a total score of four at the end of two rounds.

[UCLES 1992]

Solution	The random variable X_r can take the values 0, 1, 2 or 4 (not 3, since a bonus point is then scored). To score one in the round, the contestant must answer the first question correctly and then the second incorrectly. This gives the respective probabilities as

X_r	0	1	2	4
p	$\frac{1}{3}$	$\frac{2}{3} \times \frac{1}{3}$	$\frac{2}{3} \times \frac{2}{3} \times \frac{1}{3}$	$\frac{2}{3} \times \frac{2}{3} \times \frac{2}{3}$

(As always, we check that the probabilities have a sum of 1.
$\frac{1}{3} + \frac{2}{9} + \frac{4}{27} + \frac{8}{27} = 1$ ✔).

This gives the PGF of X_r as

$$G(t) = \frac{1}{3} + \frac{2}{9}t + \frac{4}{27}t^2 + \frac{8}{27}t^4$$

Then $$G'(t) = \frac{2}{9} + \frac{8}{27}t + \frac{32}{27}t^3$$

$$G''(t) = \frac{8}{27} + \frac{32}{9}t^2$$

This gives $$E(X) = G'(1) = \frac{2}{9} + \frac{8}{27} + \frac{32}{27} = \frac{46}{27}$$

$$\begin{aligned} \text{Var}(X) &= G''(1) + G'(1) - \left[G'(1)\right]^2 \\ &= \frac{8}{27} + \frac{32}{9} + \frac{46}{27} - \left(\frac{46}{27}\right)^2 \\ &= 2\frac{476}{729} \end{aligned}$$

The PGF of $X_1 + X_2$ is $G(t)\,F(t)$, i.e.

$$\left(\tfrac{1}{3}+\tfrac{2}{9}\,t\ +\ \tfrac{4}{27}\,t^2\ +\ \tfrac{8}{27}\,t^4\right)^2$$

The probability of a total score of 4 at the end of two rounds is the coefficient of t^4 in the above expansion, which is

$$\tfrac{1}{3}\times\tfrac{8}{27}\ +\ \tfrac{4}{27}\times\tfrac{4}{27}\ +\ \tfrac{8}{27}\times\tfrac{1}{3}\ =\ \tfrac{160}{729}$$

Once you've been through these, have a go yourself at the exercises below.

Appendix: Variance

We use the fact that $E[X(X-1)\dots(X-k+1)]=G^{(k)}(1)$ for $k\geq1$,

where $G^{(k)}(t)$ is the kth derivative of $G(t)$ with respect to t.

Then $\quad E(X)\ =G'(1)$

and $\quad E[X(X-1)]\ =\ G''(1)$

But $\quad E[X(X-1)]\ =\ E[X^2-X]$

$$=\ E(X^2)-E(X)\ \Rightarrow\ G''(1)\ =E(X^2)-E(X)$$
$$\Rightarrow\ E(X^2)\ =G''(1)+E(X)$$
$$=G''(1)+G'(1)$$
$$\Rightarrow\ E(X^2)\ =G''(1)-G'(1)$$

Finally, $\quad \text{Var}(X)\quad =\ E(X^2)-[E(X)]^2$

$$=\ G''(1)-G'(1)-[G'(1)]^2$$

EXERCISES

1 Give the PGF for the following probability distributions

(i)

X_i	0	1	2	3	4
P_i	$\frac{1}{8}$	$\frac{1}{8}$	$\frac{1}{4}$	$\frac{1}{3}$	$\frac{1}{6}$

(ii)

X_i	2	4	6
P_i	$\frac{1}{3}$	$\frac{1}{3}$	$\frac{1}{3}$

2 The random variable X has PGF

$$G(z)\ =\ \frac{z}{2-z}$$

Find the mean and variance of X.

3 The random variable X has PGF

$$G(t) = \frac{a}{b - 2t}$$

If $E(X) = 4$, find the constants a and b, $b \neq 2$.

4 A fair coin is tossed repeatedly until two heads occur consecutively. The random variable X represents the number of tosses up to and including the two consecutive heads. Calculate the probabilities that

(i) $X = 2$ (ii) $X = 3$ (iii) $X = 4$ (iv) $X = 5$ (v) $X = 6$

The PGF for X is given by

$$G(z) = \frac{z^2}{4 - 2z - z^2}$$

Calculate $E(X)$

[UCLES, 1983]

5 A random variable X has a distribution given by

$$P(X = r) = \frac{e^{-\lambda}\lambda^r}{r!}, \, r = 0, 1, 2, \ldots$$

where λ is a positive constant. Find the PGF of X and hence the mean and variance of X.

An independent random variable Y has a distribution given by

$$P(Y = r) = \frac{e^{-\mu}\mu^r}{r!}, \, r = 0, 1, 2, \ldots$$

where μ is a positive constant. Show that the PGF of $X + Y$ is given by $G(t)$, where

$$G(t) = e^{(\lambda + \mu)(t - 1)}$$

Given that $\lambda = 1$ and $\mu = 2$, find $P(X + Y = 4)$

[The relationship between the PGFs of X, Y and $X + Y$ may be quoted without proof.]

[UCLES, 1992]

6 When a die is thrown, event A occurs with probability p, the random variable N is defined by:

'The event A occurs for the first time on the Nth throw.'

Write down an expression for $P(N = n)$.

Show that $G(t)$, the PGF for N, is given by

$$G(t) = \frac{pt}{1 - qt}, \text{ where } p + q = 1$$

Deduce, in terms of p, the value of $E(N)$ and show that $\text{Var}(N) = \dfrac{q}{p^2}$.

An unbiased die is thrown repeatedly until a five and a six have been obtained. The random variable M denotes the number of throws required (thus for the sequence of results $\underline{6}$, 3, 1, 3, 6, 6, $\underline{5}$ the value of M is 7). Show that $E(M) = 9$ and calculate $\text{Var}(M)$.

[SMP, 1985]

7 An unbiased die is thrown repeatedly. The random variable R is the number of the throw at which the first six appears, and the random variable T is the number of the throw at which the second six appears.

(i) Show that the probability generating function for R is given by $G(z) = z(6 - 5z)^{-1}$.

(ii) Find $E(R)$ and $\text{Var}(R)$.

(iii) Write down the probability that exactly one six occurs in the first $t - 1$ throws, where $t > 1$, and deduce that the probability that the second six occurs on the tth throw is $(t - 1)5^{t-2}6^{-t}$.

[UCLES, 1984]

8 A and B play a game in which the probability that A scores a point is a ($0 \le a < 1$) at each turn and the probability that B scores is b ($0 < b < 1$) at each turn. The two players alternate, with A taking the first turn. The game finishes when the first point is scored.

(i) Show that the probability that A wins is $\dfrac{a}{a + b - ab}$.

(ii) If $a = 0.1$ and $b = 0.2$, show that X, the total number of turns in the game, has probability function

$$P(X = n) = \begin{cases} \dfrac{1}{10}(0.72)^{\frac{n-1}{2}} & \text{for odd } n \\[2mm] \dfrac{18}{100}(0.72)^{\frac{n-2}{2}} & \text{for even } n \end{cases}$$

(iii) Obtain the probability generating function of X and hence show that the mean number of turns in this game is seven, to the nearest integer.

[Oxford and Cambridge, 1995]

SUMMARY   When you have finished this section you should:

- be familiar with the concept of a probability generating function
- know that the probability generating function can be written
  $$G(t) = p_0 + p_1 t + p_2 t^2 + \ldots$$
- know that the mean is calculated by
  $$E(X) = G'(1)$$
- know that the variance is found using
  $$\mathrm{Var}(X) = G''(1) + G'(1) - [G'(1)]^2$$
- be able to derive the PGF for each of the geometric, Poisson and binomial distributions
- be able to use the above to find the mean and variance for each of the three distributions
- know that $G(1) = 1$
- know that $G(-1) = \Sigma$ prob. (evens) $- \Sigma$ prob. (odds)
- be able to combine these ideas with work from other sections of the syllabus.

9

Confidence intervals and tests

We begin this section by introducing a new distribution, the *F-distribution*, named in honour of the distinguished statistician, Sir Ronald Fisher. Values of this distribution are tabulated and are given in the formula sheet. Using this table, we shall be able to compare two sample variances. This is an extension of the work in the last module where we used a table of the χ^2-distribution to compare the value of a single sample variance with a given value.

We shall also extend our range of hypothesis tests to include a comparison of means of normal populations with an unknown common variance. This involves further use of the *t*-distribution introduced in the previous module. We can compare either two unrelated sets of data or two sets of paired data – the latter case gives a more powerful test.

By the end of this section you will be able to

● use the *F*-distribution

● carry out paired and unpaired *t*-tests and know when to use each.

The *F*-distribution

Suppose we take a large number of samples of a particular size from a normal population. For each of these samples we find the mean and we form a grouped frequency distribution using equal group sizes. We then plot the results as a series of histograms. (A computer is useful for this.) Eventually we have a result that looks something like Figure 9.1.

Figure 9.1

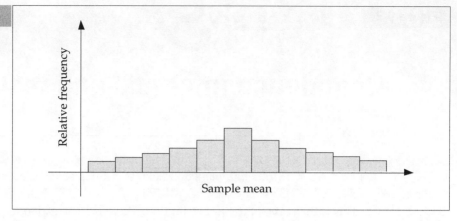

If we smooth out the distribution by joining the mid-points of the tops of the rectangles, we find the familiar shape of a normal curve.

Figure 9.2

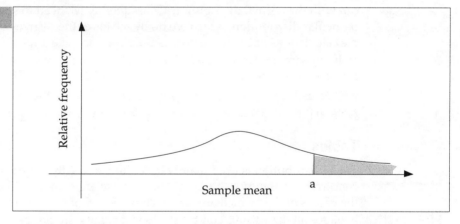

Once we have standardised our variable, we can use tables to find the probability that the sample mean exceeds any given value. We could calculate, for example, the shaded area above, which is the probability that

$$\overline{X} > a.$$

Now suppose that from the same normal distribution we take a sample of size n_1 and another of size n_2. This time, instead of the sample means, we calculate the sample variances, s_1^2 and s_2^2, and find the ratio $\dfrac{s_1^2}{s_2^2}$. Since they are both estimates of the same population variance, the expected value of this ratio is one. In practice, of course, the sample variances are never exactly the same. Half of the time the ratio is between 0 and 1 (the variances cannot be negative) and half of the time the ratio is bigger than 1. This gives a curve which is skewed to the right.

Figure 9.3

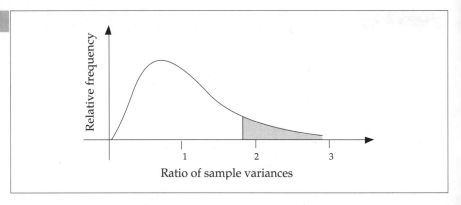

This is the curve of the *F*-distribution. There is a corresponding table of values in the formula booklet.

We cannot transform any *F*-distribution into one standard function as we can with the normal distribution. Consequently we need to specify the particular distribution, which we do by means of the degrees of freedom in the calculations of the respective sample variances, i.e. $(n_1 - 1)$ and $(n_2 - 1)$. So if our samples were of size 11 and 21, for example, we would look at the *F*-distribution with parameters $11 - 1 = 10$ and $21 - 1 = 20$. This is generally written as $F_{10,20}$ (you may see F_{20}^{10} in questions set by other exam boards). Note that the order is important: $F_{10,20}$ is not the same as $F_{20,10}$.

Tables

The *F*-distribution is used mainly in conjunction with a hypothesis test concerning variances. This being the case, we are not really interested in all the values of $F_{a,b}$ (which anyway would mean that we would need a whole book for all the various combinations instead of a single sheet). Our main concern is the small set of significant values – the critical values of the distribution corresponding to a probability of 1%, 5%, 10% etc. With the help of these, we can see whether a given ratio of sample variances could reasonably have come from a single population (or two populations with the same variance).

For example, suppose one sample of 11 items gave a sample variance of 3 and another sample of 21 items, gave a sample variance of 1.2. The first sample variance is $\frac{3}{1.2} = 2.5$ times greater than the second sample variance. Is this significant or could we get this result by chance, even though the underlying variance is the same? We look up $F_{10,20}$, being careful to take 10 as the column and 20 as the row. This gives a value of 2.35 at the 5% significance level and a value of 3.37 at the 1% significance level for a one-tailed test.

Figure 9.4

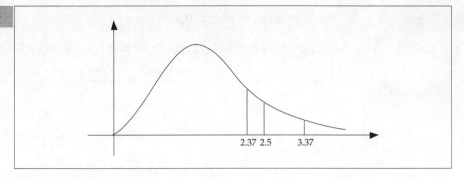

Our value lies in the 5% critical region but not in the 1% critical region, i.e. it is a significant result but not a highly significant result. Depending upon our significance level, we would or would not accept the two samples as coming from populations with the same variance.

Have a look at the table for the *F*-distribution and check that you agree with the following:

(i) $F_{3,7}$ > 4.35   with probability 0.05   3 on top (v_1)
                                                        7 on side (v_2)

        > 8.45   with probability 0.01

(ii) $F_{5,3}$ > 9.01   at 5% level

        > 28.24   at 1% level

(iii) Sample size 7 and sample size 12 respectively.

This gives the degrees of freedom as 7 – 1 = 6 and 12 – 1 = 11, so $F_{6,11}$

critical values are 3.09 (5%) and 5.07 (1%).

Intervals

We may be interested in finding *p* and *q* such that

$$P(p < X < q) = 0.9$$

when *X* has an *F*-distribution with v_1 and v_2 degrees of freedom, i.e. F_{v_1, v_2}. In this case, we make use of the property

$$F_{v_1, v_2}(\alpha) = \frac{1}{F_{v_2, v_1}} (100 - \alpha\%)$$

So that, for example, $F_{3,7}$ at 5% = $\dfrac{1}{F_{7,3}}$ at 95%

Since $F_{3,7}$ at 5% = 4.35, this gives

$$F_{7,3}(95\%) = \frac{1}{4.35} = 0.23$$

Now suppose we had to find p and q so that $P(p < X < q) = 0.9$ where $X \sim F_{8,5}$

Figure 9.5

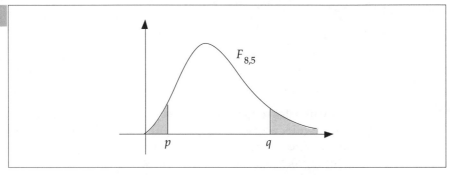

We split the tail equally, so that each of the shaded areas is 0.05. From the 0.05 F-table, we have $F_{8,5} = 4.82 = q$.

To find p, we want $F_{8,5}(95\%)$.

Using the formula, this is $\dfrac{1}{F_{5,8}}(5\%) = \dfrac{1}{3.69} = 0.27 = p$

i.e. the required interval is $0.27 < X < 4.82$

Hypothesis testing

As mentioned earlier, the main use of the F-distribution is for testing hypotheses concerning variances of populations. We do this by taking samples from the two populations and calculating the sample variances, s_1^2 and s_2^2, say. The point is that the ratio $\dfrac{s_1^2}{s_2^2}$ has only an F-distribution *if* the underlying variances are the same. So we conclude that the variances are significantly different only if the value $\dfrac{s_1^2}{s_2^2}$ $\left(\text{or } \dfrac{s_2^2}{s_1^2} \right)$ is greater than the critical value for the particular F-distribution, i.e. is unlikely to be part of this F-distribution. We can summarise the procedure as

(i) Find s_1^2 and s_2^2

(ii) State hypotheses: H_0: $\sigma_1^2 = \sigma_2^2$

H_1: $\sigma_1^2 > \sigma_2^2$ one-tailed

$\sigma_1^2 < \sigma_2^2$

or H_1: $\sigma_1^2 \neq \sigma_2^2$ two-tailed

(iii) Look up the critical value of F with $(n_1 - 1)$ and $(n_2 - 1)$ degrees of freedom. If two-tailed, the α-level is halved (e.g. a 10% significance is a 5% test if two-tailed).

(iv) For a one-tailed test, calculate $\dfrac{s_1^2}{s_2^2}$ or $\dfrac{s_2^2}{s_1^2}$ as appropriate.

For a two-tailed test, put the larger estimate as the numerator (since the table gives values of the ratio > 1).

(v) Compare with critical F-value and draw conclusions

Assumptions

As with most hypothesis tests, there are conditions which must be satisfied. For the F-test we assume that the populations from which the samples are drawn are distributed normally and the samples are random and independent.

Here's an example.

Example

Two machines produce ball-bearings with a nominal diameter of 10 mm. The diameters of a sample taken from each machine are as follows:

Machine X: 10.027   10.028   10.031   10.022   10.028   10.021   10.026

Machine Y: 10.010   10.027   10.020   10.007   10.016   10.008   10.021   10.017

The diameters of ball-bearings produced by machines X and Y are respectively $N(\mu_1, \sigma_1^2)$ and $N(\mu_2, \sigma_2^2)$. It is known that $\mu_1 \neq \mu_2$. Show that, on the basis of the above data, there is no reason to doubt that $\sigma_1^2 = \sigma_2^2$.

[UCLES, 1984]

Solution

The assumptions for the F-test are satisfied, i.e. the populations are normally distributed and the data sets are independent.

Hypotheses: H_0: $\sigma_1^2 = \sigma_2^2$

H_1: $\sigma_1^2 \neq \sigma_2^2$

It's a two-tailed test since there is no indication of a definite direction, and we can use a 10% significance level.

We work out the variances first of all. (Note that we can code the data, i.e. ignore the 10, when working out $x\sigma_{n-1}$ with a calculator.)

$$s_x = 0.003532 \quad \text{with } 7 - 1 = 6 \text{ degrees of freedom.}$$
$$s_y = 0.007005 \quad \text{with } 8 - 1 = 7 \text{ degrees of freedom.}$$

Since s_y is the larger, we need $F_{7,6}$ (5%), which from the tables is 4.22 (averaging).

Our test statistic is $\quad F = \dfrac{s_y^2}{s_x^2} = \dfrac{0.007005^2}{0.003532^2} = 3.93$ and this assumes a 10% significance level.

This is not significant and there is no reason, on the evidence, to doubt that the variances are the same.

Here is another example, this time one-tailed.

Example

Each of a random sample of nine students was subjected to a stimulus and the reaction time (in seconds) was measured with the following results:

Reaction time	0.37	0.41	0.39	0.51	0.67	0.41	0.36	0.45	0.62

A second sample of seven students were tested five minutes after they had each drunk a pint of beer. The corresponding results were

Reaction time	0.41	0.72	0.81	0.59	0.38	0.62	0.35

Test at the 5% level whether the data show an increase in variability in students who had recently had a drink.

Solution

$$n_1 = 9 \quad s_1^2 = 0.0125 \quad \text{(using a calculator)}$$
$$n_2 = 7 \quad s_2^2 = 0.0319 \quad \text{(using a calculator)}$$
$$H_0: \quad \sigma_1^2 = \sigma_2^2$$
$$H_1: \quad \sigma_2^2 > \sigma_1^2$$

One-tailed test, $7 - 1 = 6$ and $9 - 1 = 8$ degrees of freedom at the 5% level. (Note that the larger estimate comes before the smaller.)

$$F_{6,8} (5\%) = 3.58$$

Our test statistic is

$$F = \frac{0.0319}{0.0125} = 2.55$$

This is not a significant result and we do not reject the null hypothesis. On the basis of these results we would not infer that the variability has increased.

We are now going to look at a different type of hypothesis test, concerning two population means. Before we start, we need to learn how to continue two sample variances to form a single estimate for the underlying population variance.

Pooled estimate for population variance

You may already be familiar with the idea of a *weighted average*. If six items have an average of 5.3 and a further 12 items have an average of 4.7, we form an overall estimate of the average by calculating

$$\frac{6 \times 5.3 + 12 \times 4.7}{6 + 12} = 4.9$$

The name weighted average comes from the fact that the two means 5.3 and 4.7 are multiplied, or *weighted*, by their corresponding sample size: the bigger the sample size, the more weight, or importance, is given to the sample mean.

In a similar fashion, we can combine two different estimates for the same variance to give an overall estimate. If one sample of size n_1 gives an unbiased estimate of s_1^2 and another sample of size n_2 gives an unbiased estimate of s_2^2, then a pooled estimate of the common population variance is given by

$$s^2 = \frac{(n_1 - 1)\, s_1^2 + (n_2 - 1)\, s_2^2}{(n_1 - 1) + (n_2 - 1)}$$

This is also an unbiased estimate. The weights in this case are slightly different: they are in fact the respective degrees of freedom for the estimates s_1^2 and s_2^2.

Example

Samples of size 10 and 17 from different populations gave unbiased estimates for the variance of 9.8 and 8.1 respectively. Assuming that the underlying variance is the same, give a pooled estimate of its value.

Solution

$$s^2 = \frac{(10 - 1)\, 9.8 + (17 - 1)\, 8.11}{(10 - 1) + (17 - 1)}$$

$$= \frac{9 \times 9.8 + 16 \times 8.1}{25} = 8.7 \ (1 \text{ d.p.})$$

We expect the answer to be between the two sample variances (and more towards the value derived from the bigger sample size), as it is in this case. This is a quick check that is easy to carry out and helps to rule out slips with the calculator.

We can now combine and see how we can compare the means of two distributions.

The difference of two means

Much of the practical side of statistics is concerned with means: estimating the population mean, comparing the sample mean with a fixed value, and so on. In this section we shall be comparing the means of samples drawn from two different populations. The assumptions that we need to make for the analysis are (i) that the populations are normally distributed and (ii) that they have the same variance.

The derivation follows the same steps that we used in the introduction to the t-distribution. Firstly, we found the normal distribution of the variable with known variance. This was then standardised to give a N(0,1) distribution. Finally, we substituted an estimate for the variance for the known population variance. In doing this, the standardised normal distribution became a t-distribution with the appropriate number of degrees of freedom.

Suppose we have two variables, X and Y, which have normal distributions. Their means are different but they have the same variance, σ^2. We can write

$$X \sim N(\mu_x, \sigma^2) \text{ and } Y \sim N(\mu_y, \sigma^2)$$

Now suppose we take a sample from each, of size n_1 from X and size n_2 from Y. The distribution of the means of these samples will be

$$\bar{X} \sim N\left(\mu_x, \frac{\sigma^2}{n_1}\right) \text{ and } \bar{Y} \sim N\left(\mu_y, \frac{\sigma^2}{n_2}\right)$$

If we now subtract these distributions, remembering to add the variances, we have

$$\bar{X} - \bar{Y} \sim N\left(\mu_x - \mu_y, \frac{\sigma^2}{n_1} + \frac{\sigma^2}{n_2}\right)$$

We have completed the first stage and found the distribution of the variable we want, the difference between the means. We now standardise this normal variable, to give

$$\frac{(\bar{X} - \bar{Y}) - (\mu_x - \mu_y)}{\sqrt{\dfrac{\sigma^2}{n_1} + \dfrac{\sigma^2}{n_2}}} \sim N(0,1)$$

Finally, we substitute our unbiased estimate s^2 for the population variance σ^2. The denominator becomes

$$\sqrt{\frac{s^2}{n_1} + \frac{s^2}{n_2}} = \sqrt{s^2\left(\frac{1}{n_1} + \frac{1}{n_2}\right)} = s\sqrt{\frac{1}{n_1} + \frac{1}{n_2}}$$

and the variable

$$\frac{(\bar{X}-\bar{Y})-(\mu_x-\mu_y)}{s\sqrt{\dfrac{1}{n_1}+\dfrac{1}{n_2}}}$$

has a t-distribution. We have $n_1 + n_2$ independent observations and two calculated means $\bar{X}$ and $\bar{Y}$, so we have $n_1 + n_2 - 2$ degrees of freedom. The value of s^2 comes from a pooled estimate of the variance of σ^2 that we looked at in the previous section. From this distribution and the tables, we can work out a confidence interval for the difference between means. We will also be able to test whether this difference could have a particular value. In particular, it is useful to see whether the means of the populations could be the same, i.e. that the difference is zero.

Confidence interval

We can break down the construction of our confidence interval into a series of steps.

(i) For the given data from the two samples we calculate the means $\bar{x}$, $\bar{y}$ and the unbiased estimates for the variance s_1^2, s_2^2.

(ii) We find a pooled estimate for the variance (which we are assuming is the same for both the populations):

$$s^2 = \frac{(n_1-1)\,s_1^2 + (n_2-1)\,s_2^2}{n_1 + n_2 - 2}$$

(iii) We find the value of t from the tables which corresponds to $(n_1 + n_2 - 2)$ degrees of freedom and the given confidence level. Since we normally expect to give a symmetric interval, we split the remainder equally between the two tails. For example, with a 95% confidence level, the 5% remaining is halved and we look at the $2\frac{1}{2}\% = 0.025$ column of the t-table.

(iv) We give the confidence interval as

$$(\bar{x}-\bar{y}) \pm t^* \times s\sqrt{\frac{1}{n_1}+\frac{1}{n_2}}$$

where t^* is the appropriate t-value.

Here is an example of this.

Example   Two samples are drawn from normal populations and are summarised by:

Sample 1: $\Sigma x = 212$ Sample 2: $\Sigma y = 243$

153

$$\Sigma x^2 = 4042 \qquad\qquad \Sigma y^2 = 4128$$

size 16 \qquad\qquad size 20

Give a 95% symmetrical confidence interval for the difference between the means, assuming that the variances are the same for both populations.

| **Solution** | |

(i) $\bar{x} = \dfrac{\Sigma x}{n_1} = \dfrac{212}{16} = 13.25$ \qquad $\bar{y} = \dfrac{\Sigma y}{n_2} = \dfrac{243}{20} = 12.15$

$s_1^2 = \dfrac{16}{15}\left[\dfrac{\Sigma x^2}{16} - \bar{x}^2\right] = 82.200$ \qquad $s_2^2 = \dfrac{20}{19}\left[\dfrac{\Sigma y^2}{20} - \bar{y}^2\right] = 61.871$

(ii) The pooled estimate for the population variance

$$s^2 = \dfrac{(16-1)\,82.200 + (20-1)\,61.871}{16+20-2} = 70.84 \text{ (2 d.p.)}$$

(iii) We want a 95% confidence interval, so $2\frac{1}{2}\%$ or 0.025 in each tail. There are 34 degrees of freedom, and from the tables t_{34} (2.5%) = 2.032.

(iv) The confidence interval for the difference between the means is then

$$(13.25 - 12.15) \pm 2.032 \times \sqrt{70.84\left(\tfrac{1}{16} + \tfrac{1}{20}\right)}$$

i.e. 1.10 ± 5.74 or $(-4.64, 6.84)$

Note that this confidence interval includes the value of zero, the case when the means of the two populations are the same. A very useful application of the t-distribution is testing to see whether the means of the populations could be equal.

Hypothesis test

Generally we use the test to see whether it is reasonable to assume that the means of the underlying populations are the same. We can easily extend this to see whether the difference of the means is a particular value (other than zero).

Assumptions

Before using the test, we must be sure that:

- the samples are random and independent of each other
- the populations are normally distributed, and
- the underlying variances are the same.

(We can use an F-test if we want to test the third assumption.)

If these conditions are satisfied, the procedure to test whether the means of two populations are the same can be summarised as:

(i)   Take samples from each of the populations, and find the sample mean and variance for each.

(ii) Calculate the pooled estimate for the population variance (under the assumption that the underlying variance is the same for each population).

(iii) Determine whether a one- or two-tailed test is appropriate.

(iv) Give appropriate null and alternative hypotheses.

(v)   Find the critical t-value with $(n_1 - 1) + (n_2 - 1)$ degrees of freedom at the given significance level.

(vi) Calculate the test-statistic.

$$t = \frac{\bar{x} - \bar{y}}{s\sqrt{\dfrac{1}{n_1} + \dfrac{1}{n_2}}}$$

where s^2 is the pooled estimate for the population variance.

(viii) Compare and conclude.

Here are some examples which use these ideas.

Example

Two types of composite carbon fibre, each consisting of seven strands, are compared for strength. A 100 mm length of fibre is clamped in a rig and an increasing load applied until the fibre breaks. The breaking loads for a random sample of 13 lengths of type A and a random sample of 10 lengths of type B are shown in the following table.

	Breaking load (in suitable units)						
Type A	724	751	784	794	794	794	
	804	817	829	834	839	839	839
Type B	646	687	720	727	751		
	761	789	794	817	817		

(i)   Using a 5% significance level, test whether the two types of fibre have the same mean breaking strength. State the null and alternative hypotheses as well as two assumptions you are making.

(ii) Find the 90% two-sided symmetric confidence interval for the difference in mean breaking loads between the two types of carbon fibre.

[Oxford and Cambridge 1995]

Solution

The assumptions are that the loads are normally distributed and that the two types have equal variances. There is no indication of direction in the question, so the test is two-tailed.

$$H_0: \ \mu_A = \mu_B$$
$$H_1: \ \mu_A \neq \mu_B$$

With $13 + 10 - 2 = 21$ degrees of freedom and a two-tailed test, $t_{21}(2.5\%) = 2.08$

Using a calculator, $\bar{A} = 803.23 \quad s_A = 35.67$ (2 d.p.)

$$\bar{B} = 750.9 \quad s_B = 56.53 \text{ (2 d.p.)}$$

Our pooled estimate for the variance is

$$s^2 = \frac{(13-1)\,35.67^2 + (10-1)\,56.53^2}{13 + 10 - 2}$$

$$= 2096.6 \text{ (1 d.p.)}$$

The test statistic is

$$t = \frac{\bar{A} - \bar{B}}{s\sqrt{\dfrac{1}{n_A} + \dfrac{1}{n_B}}} = \frac{803.23 - 750.9}{\sqrt{2096.6\left(\frac{1}{13} + \frac{1}{10}\right)}} = \frac{52.33}{19.26} = 2.7 \text{ (1 d.p.)}$$

This is a significant result and we reject the null hypothesis. The evidence suggests a difference in mean breaking strength at the 5% level.

A 90% confidence interval for the difference in mean breaking loads is given by

$$(\bar{A} - \bar{B}) \pm t_{21}(5\%)\, s\sqrt{\frac{1}{n_A} + \frac{1}{n_B}}$$

i.e. $52.33 \pm 1.721 \times 19.26$

or $(19.2, 85.5)$ (1 d.p.)

Example	A golfer calculated that, for his last eight rounds of golf, $\Sigma x = 720$, $\Sigma(x - \bar{x})^2 = 512$, where x denotes his score in a round. In order to improve his golf (i.e. to make his scores smaller), he attended a series of lessons. For the first four rounds after these lessons he calculated that $\Sigma y = 340$, $\Sigma(y - \bar{y})^2 = 144$, where y denotes his score in a round after having lessons. Use a t-test to determine whether or not on the evidence of these two samples the lessons had produced, at the 10% level, a significant improvement in his golf. State the assumptions made in using this test.

[UCLES 1981]

Solution	We have been given the data in an alternative form here: in order to find s_x^2 we use the definition of an unbiased estimate for σ^2,

$$s_x^2 = \frac{\Sigma(x - \bar{x})^2}{n-1}$$

For the given data, we find

$$n_1 = 8, \ \bar{x} = \frac{\Sigma x}{n_1} = \frac{720}{8} = 90, \ s_x^2 = \frac{\Sigma(x-\bar{x})^2}{n_1-1} = \frac{512}{7}$$

$$n_2 = 4, \ \bar{y} = \frac{340}{4} = 85, \ s_y^2 = \frac{144}{3} = 48$$

We now need a pooled estimate for the common variance (a necessary assumption to make when using this test is that the two populations have equal variances), given by

$$s^2 = \frac{(n_1-1)\,s_x^2 + (n_2-1)\,s_y^2}{n_1 + n_2 - 2}$$

$$= \frac{7 \times \frac{512}{7} + 3 \times \frac{144}{3}}{8+4-2} = \frac{656}{10} = 65.6$$

There is a definite indication in the wording of the question of a direction ('improvement'), so the test is one-tailed.

$$H_0: \ \mu_x = \mu_y$$
$$H_1: \ \mu_x > \mu_y$$

We have $8 + 4 - 2 = 10$ degrees of freedom, and at the 10% level, one-tailed, our critical t-value is

$$t_{10}\,(10\%) = 1.372$$

Our test statistic is

$$t = \frac{90-85}{\sqrt{65.6\left(\frac{1}{8}+\frac{1}{4}\right)}} = 1.01 \ \ (2 \text{ d.p.})$$

This is not a significant result and we do not reject the null hypothesis. On the given evidence, there is no reason to suppose that the lessons are improving his golf scores. The assumptions made in the test are that the samples are independent, that the populations are normally distributed and have the same population variance.

Example

Two independent samples, each of size n, have means $\bar{x}_1$ and $\bar{x}_2$. The values of the unbiased estimates of the population variances are s_1^2 and s_2^2 respectively. Show that the test statistic corresponding to the two-sample t-test, when testing for equality of the population means, reduces to

$$\frac{(\bar{x}_1 - \bar{x}_2)\sqrt{n}}{\sqrt{s_1^2 + s_2^2}}$$

and state the corresponding number of degrees of freedom.

Gallia melons are packed in boxes of 12 and are standardised for size. The average weight of a melon is claimed to be 600 g. A fruiterer has received two deliveries of melons from different suppliers, A and B. She suspects that the melons from A and B have different mean weights and weighs the melons from two randomly chosen boxes, one from each supplier. The mean weight $\bar{x}$, in g, and unbiased estimate of variances s^2, in g^2, are given in the table.

	$\bar{x}$	s^2
Supplier A	607.2	153.8
Supplier B	593.3	118.8

Assuming normal distributions, show that, using a 5% significance level, each sample could come from a population with mean 600 g.

Stating any further necessary assumption, test, at the 1% significance level, for a difference between the means of the two populations.

[UCLES 1995]

Solution

The test statistic for the two-sample t-test when testing for equality of the population means is

$$\frac{\bar{x}_1 - \bar{x}_2}{s\sqrt{\dfrac{1}{n_1} + \dfrac{1}{n_2}}}$$

The pooled estimate for the population variance, with $n_1 = n = n_2$ is

$$s^2 = \frac{(n-1)\,s_1^2 + (n-1)\,s_2^2}{(n-1) + (n-1)} = \frac{s_1^2 + s_2^2}{2}$$

The denominator of the fraction becomes

$$\sqrt{\frac{s_1^2 + s_2^2}{2}}\,\sqrt{\frac{1}{n} + \frac{1}{n}} = \sqrt{\left(\frac{s_1^2 + s_2^2}{2}\right)\left(\frac{2}{n}\right)} = \sqrt{\frac{s_1^2 + s_2^2}{n}}$$

Multiplying top and bottom of the fraction by $\sqrt{n}$ gives

$$\frac{(\bar{x}_1 - \bar{x}_2)\,\sqrt{n}}{\sqrt{s_1^2 + s_2^2}}$$ as required. There are $(2n - 2)$ degrees of freedom.

At the 5% level, with 11 degrees of freedom and a two-tailed test, $t_{11}\,(2.5\%) = 2.201$

The test statistic for a one-sample t-test is

$$\frac{\bar{x} - 600}{\sqrt{\dfrac{s^2}{n}}}$$

This gives: Supplier A, $\dfrac{607.2 - 600}{\sqrt{\dfrac{153.8}{12}}} = 2.01$

Supplier B, $\dfrac{593.3 - 600}{\sqrt{\dfrac{118.8}{12}}} = -2.13$

Both of these are within the critical region of ± 2.2 and so each sample could come from a population with mean 600 g.

If we assume that the variance of each population is the same we can carry out a two-sample t-test.

We have already devised the test statistic above. There is no indication of direction in the wording of the question, so we use a two-tailed test.

$$H_0:\ \mu_1 = \mu_2$$
$$H_1:\ \mu_1 \neq \mu_2$$

There are $2 \times 12 - 2 = 22$ degrees of freedom. $t_{22}\,(0.5\%) = 2.819$ from the tables.

Our test statistic is

$$t = \frac{(\bar{x}_1 - \bar{x}_2)\,\sqrt{n}}{\sqrt{s_1^2 + s_2^2}} = \frac{(607.2 - 593.3)\,\sqrt{12}}{\sqrt{153.8 + 118.8}}$$

$$= 2.92$$

This is significant at the 1% level, and we conclude that the fruiterer's suspicions are well-founded. There would appear to be a difference between the means of the two populations.

Paired *t*-test

We have seen how the *t*-test can be used to compare the means of two populations which have a normal distribution. In many such cases, there is no particular connection between a single item from one of the populations and a single item from the other. In comparing the mean life of two different brands of light-bulb, for example, it would not be particularly significant if we took a bulb from each and found that the one from Brand *A* lasted longer than that from Brand *B*. The individual differences are not so important: we would be more interested in taking samples from each and comparing the sample means.

It is a different situation when we want to assess the efficiency of some 'treatment'. In this case we are more interested in the *difference* between a pair of items. If we want to see whether extra coaching has any effect on students' ability in French, for example, we might measure the level of all the students in a class before and after the coaching. We could then analyse the resulting collection of differences and see whether they are significant. This is called a *paired sample*.

In using the differences to perform a test, we have to be careful that the two observations used to calculate the difference are independent. Carrying out the first experiment must not affect the outcome of the subsequent experiment. It would be no good, for instance, in assessing the level of the students before and after coaching to use the same test: they could be expected to improve their result on second sight even without coaching.

Even if the two *populations* are not normally distributed, we can still use the paired-sample *t*-test, provided that the *differences* have a normal distribution. This contrasts with the two-sample *t*-test where the condition is that both populations should be normally distributed. From the pairs of values, we find the differences. We can then calculate the mean $\bar{d}$ and standard deviation, s_d, of these differences and use a *t*-test to see whether the mean differs significantly from zero. Here is an example of this procedure.

| Example | The following data are the third and fourth round scores of a random sample of five competitors in an open golf tournament. |

Competitor	A	B	C	D	E
3rd round	76	75	72	75	79
4th round	70	73	71	68	76

Use a paired *t*-test and a 5% significance level to test whether there is a difference in the mean score of all the competitors on the two rounds.

[AEB 1993]

Solution

In calculating the differences it is essential to preserve the order. In this case we can subtract the fourth round from the third, which gives the differences

6, 2, 1, 7 and 3 respectively.

This usually gives a mixture of positive and negative differences, although here they are all positive. We can use a calculator to find that

$$\bar{d} = 3.80 \text{ and } s_d = 2.588$$

Our null hypothesis is that there is no difference in the scores between the rounds. There is no indication of an expected direction in the question so we use a two-tailed test

$$H_0: \bar{d} = 0$$

$$H_1: \bar{d} \neq 0$$

We have five differences, which means $5 - 1 = 4$ degrees of freedom. With a 5%, two-tailed test we need the value of t_4 (2.5%) = 2.776.

We can now calculate our test result, using

$$t = \frac{\bar{d}}{\frac{s_d}{\sqrt{n}}} = \frac{3.80}{\frac{2.588}{\sqrt{5}}} = 3.28 \text{ (2 d.p.)}$$

This is greater than the critical value and so we reject the null hypothesis. There is sufficient evidence at the 5% level to indicate a change in mean score between the rounds.

We can summarise the test before we work through another example.

Summary of procedure

Before we carry out a paired-sample *t*-test we must ensure that the distribution of the differences is *normal*. (If this condition is not met, we may need to use a non-parametric test, which is less powerful.) The samples also need to be random and independent. We then

(i) determine whether it is a one- or two-tailed test

(ii) state appropriate null and alternative hypotheses

161

(iii) determine the number of degrees of freedom, $(n-1)$, where n is the number of pairs

(iv) determine the appropriate t-value from the table

(v) work out the differences

(vi) calculate $\bar{d}$ and s_d

(vii) calculate the test statistic,

$$t = \frac{\bar{d}}{\frac{s_d}{\sqrt{n}}}$$

(viii) compare this with the critical t-value from (iv)

(ix) draw conclusions.

Here is a further example of this kind of test.

Example

Two analysers are used in a hospital laboratory to measure blood creatinine levels. These are used as a measure of kidney function.

To compare the performance of the two machines, a technician took eight specimens of blood and measured the creatinine level (in micromoles per litre) of each specimen using each machine. The results were as follows:

Specimen	1	2	3	4	5	6	7	8
Analyser A	119	173	100	99	77	121	84	73
Analyser B	106	153	83	95	69	123	84	67

The technician carried out a paired t-test and reported that there was a difference between analysers at the 5% significance level. Verify that this is in fact the case, assuming a normal distribution.

[AEB 1992]

Solution

The differences are

$$13, 20, 17, 4, 8, -2, 0, 6$$

This gives $\bar{x}_d = 8.25$ $S_d = 7.87$ (2 d.p.)

$$H_0: \quad \mu_d = 0$$
$$H_1: \quad \mu_d \neq 0 \text{ (two-tailed test)}$$

At the two-tailed 5% level, with $8 - 1 = 7$ degrees of freedom, $t_7 (2.5\%) = 2.365$.

Our test statistic is

$$\frac{\bar{x}_d}{\frac{s_d}{\sqrt{n}}} = \frac{8.25}{\frac{7.87}{\sqrt{8}}} = 2.97$$

This is significant, and confirms the technician's conclusion that there was a difference between analysers at the 5% level.

Example

An experiment was conducted to determine the effect of the weather on the amount of pollution in a river. At each of six sites along the river a sample of water was taken on a dry day and an index of pollution was determined for each sample. The sampling was repeated on a wet day. The following results were obtained.

Site number	1	2	3	4	5	6
Pollution index on dry day (x)	188	165	211	178	171	199
Pollution index on wet day (y)	170	140	132	168	172	170

Given that $\Sigma x = 1112$, $\Sigma y = 952$, $\Sigma x^2 = 207\,616$ and $\Sigma y^2 = 152\,632$, analyse the data, at a 5% level of significance (two-tailed),

(i) using a paired-sample t-test with 5 degrees of freedom,

(ii) using a two-sample t-test with 10 degrees of freedom.

State, giving a brief reason, which of these tests you consider to be more appropriate.

[UCLES 1983]

Solution

(i) The differences are

$$18 \quad 25 \quad 79 \quad 10 \quad -1 \quad 29$$

This gives $\bar{x}_d = 26.67$ and $s_d = 27.80$ (2 d.p.)

We have a 2-tailed test.

$H_0: \mu_d = 0$ and $H_1: \mu_d \neq 0$

With $6 - 1 = 5$ degrees of freedom, a two-tailed test and a 5% level of significance, our critical t-value is

$$t_5 (2.5\%) = 2.571$$

Our test statistic is $\dfrac{\overline{x}_s}{\frac{s_d}{\sqrt{n}}} = \dfrac{26.67}{\frac{27.8}{\sqrt{6}}} = 2.35$ (2 d.p.)

This is not significant and we accept the null hypothesis. There is no reason to think that the weather affects pollution on the basis of the evidence.

(ii) We have $\overline{x} = \dfrac{1112}{6} = 185.3$, $s_x^2 = 305.1$ (1 d.p.)

$\overline{y} = 158.7$, $s_y^2 = 316.3$ (1 d.p.)

Since the sample sizes are the same, we can average the two estimates for our pooled estimate of the variance,

$$s^2 = \dfrac{305.1 + 316.3}{2} = 310.7 \text{ (1 d.p.)}$$

Our new test is

$H_0: \mu_x = \mu_y$

$H_1: \mu_x \neq \mu_y$

Two-tailed, 5% significance, 10 degrees of freedom,

$t_{10}(2.5\%) = 2.228$

Our test statistic is $\dfrac{\mu_x - \mu_y}{\sqrt{s^2\left(\frac{1}{n_1} + \frac{1}{n_2}\right)}} = \dfrac{26.6}{\sqrt{310.7\left(\frac{2}{6}\right)}}$

$$= 2.6 \text{ (1 d.p.)}$$

This is a significant result and we reject the null hypothesis. The evidence suggests that weather affects pollution. Since the data are independent pairs of readings, we would expect the paired-sample *t*-test to be the more appropriate.

EXERCISES

1 From the tables, find (i) $F_{3,6}$ (0.05) and (ii) $F_{6,3}$ (0.05)

2 Find m such that $P(X > m) = 0.01$ if X has a

(i) $F_{4,6}$ distribution

(ii) $F_{2,14}$ distribution.

3 Find p and q such that

$$P(p < X < q) = 0.9$$

where X has a $F_{6,4}$ distribution.

4 The light attenuation of trees may be measured by photometric methods, which are very time consuming, or by photographic techniques which are much quicker.

The light attenuation of an oak tree was repeatedly measured by both methods independently. The following results, expressed as percentages, were obtained:

Photometric	85.6	86.1	86.5	85.1	86.8	87.3	
Photographic	82.4	84.7	86.1	87.2	82.4	85.8	84.3

Assuming normal distribution, test at the 10% significance level whether there is a difference in

(i)   the variability of the two methods,

(ii)   the mean measurement by the two methods.

[AEB 1993]

5 In a chemical plant, a certain product is made by two processes. The product always contains a small amount of impurity and it is desired to see whether the processes are equally variable in terms of the percentage of impurity in the product.

The percentages of impurity in a random sample of 10 batches of the product made by one process were:

4.4   3.6   4.8   2.8   4.4   4.1   3.9   4.2   4.5   5.1

and the percentages of impurity in a random sample of 8 batches made by the other process were:

3.5   4.7   4.1   5.6   4.8   3.4   5.4   4.7

Test at the 1% level of significance whether it is reasonable to assume that the underlying population variances are equal. State your null and alternative hypotheses and the critical value of your test statistic at the 1% level of significance.

State the assumptions about the underlying distributions that are required for your analysis to be satisfactory.

In the light of the result of your test, would you be prepared to use a *t*-test to examine whether the underlying population means are equal? Explain why.

[MEI 1992]

6 To test whether a new version of a computer programming language enabled faster task completion, the same task was performed by 16 programmers, divided at random into two groups. The first group used the new version of the language, and the time for task completion, in hours, for each programmer was as follows:

4.9   6.3   9.6   5.2   4.1   7.2   4.0

The second group used the old version, and their times were summarised as follows:

$n = 9$, $\Sigma x = 71.2$, $\Sigma x^2 = 604.92$

(a)   State the null and alternative hypotheses.

(b)   Perform an appropriate test at the 5% level of significance.

In order to compare like with like, experiments such as this are often performed using the same individuals in the first and the second groups.

(c)   Give a reason why this strategy would not be appropriate in this case.

[ULEAC 1996]

7 Machinery is supplied to a factory with parts already assembled, and secured by nuts and bolts. For the nut and bolt pairs, the effective diameter of the bolt should be on average 0.6 mm less than that of its nut. The diameters of the nuts and the bolts may be assumed to follow a normal distribution. A quality control engineer suspected that the difference between the diameters of a batch of nuts and their bolts was too great, and she recorded the data shown in the table.

Assembly no.	1	2	3	4
Diameter of bolt (mm)	4.03	4.08	4.00	4.00
Diameter of nut (mm)	4.75	4.88	4.90	5.01

Test at the 5% level whether there is any evidence for the engineer's suspicions, stating the null and alternative hypotheses.

[ULEAC 1996]

8 State conditions under which it is valid to use the two-sample (i.e. unpaired) *t*-test to test for a difference between the means of two populations.

Ten hospital patients, selected at random, were given a drug *A* and their reaction times, in milliseconds, to a certain stimulus were measured with the following results:

303   289   291   288   293   280   285   297   283   298

Ten other patients were given drug *B* and their reaction times to the same stimulus were:

295   294   278   291   284   282   275   293   272   283

Assuming that the necessary conditions apply, show that the data do not provide evidence at the 5% significance level of a difference between mean reaction times after the administration of the two drugs.

In fact the two sets of figures had been obtained from the same ten patients in the same order. Carry out a more appropriate *t*-test, using a 5% significance level.

[UCLES 1992]

9 Eight candidates for entrance to a private school are given two test-papers which are thought to be of the same level of difficulty. Their scores are given in the following table.

Candidate	1	2	3	4	5	6	7	8
Paper I score	106	110	120	120	106	105	98	114
Paper II score	104	114	112	114	92	105	102	117

Carry out the appropriate *t*-test to determine whether the papers are of equivalent degree of difficulty, stating your assumptions and hypotheses carefully.

[Oxford 1989]

SUMMARY When you have finished this section, you should:

- be able to look up appropriate values in the F-table

- know how to find p and q given that $P(p < X < q) = 0.9$ and X has an F-distribution

- be able to carry out a hypothesis test for the equality of two pulation variances, using the F-distribution

- be able to calculate a pooled estimate for a common population variance given two sample variances

- know that the conditions necessary to carry out an F-test are that the populations have a normal distribution and that the samples are random and independent

- know that the conditions necessary to carry out an unpaired-sample t-test are that the populations have (approximately at least) normal distributions, that they have equal variances and that the samples are random and independent

- be able to carry out an unpaired-sample t-test on the equality of two population means

- be able to give a confidence interval for the difference between two population means, given the necessary conditions

- be able to give examples of where a paired t-test is appropriate

- know that the conditions necessary in order to carry out this test are that the differences are distributed normally and that the samples are random and independent

- know that a paired t-test is more powerful than an unpaired t-test

- know the procedure for carrying out a paired t-test.

10

Analysis of variance

We have already seen how we can test whether two means are the same using the *t*-test. When we want to compare several means, the situation is a little different. Testing each of the possible pairs is not a practical proposition: even with four means we would have to carry out six tests. The number of tests necessary increases rapidly with a greater number of means. Also, the data for these tests are used over and over again, and it becomes increasingly likely that we may draw incorrect conclusions. Analysis of variance (hereafter ANOVA) provides a *single test* for determining whether all of a collection of means are the same or not.

By the end of this section you will be able to

● use analysis of variance to determine whether variations between groups of means are significant

● explain when to use a one-way and when to use a two-way ANOVA.

The basic model

Generally, the random variables we study have a single source of variation. Suppose, for example, that the mean of a population is 12 and we draw some typical examples from the population – say 12.2, 12.5, 11.6, 11.9, 12.5 … Here the variation is confined to the naturally occurring variation between items, so that the value of a particular item x_i could be written

$$x_i = \mu + \varepsilon_i$$

where μ is the mean (12 in this case) and ε_i the individual variation from the mean.

Now suppose that the population has a mean of 12 but comprises two groups: one with a mean of 11 and the other a mean of 13. Typical items could now be 11.2, 10.7, 13.5, 10.9, 12.7 … the values of which are now composed of the sum of three parts: the overall mean (12), an additional factor arising from membership of one or other of the groups (±1) and the individual variation. In general, if there are j groups and if x_{ij} means the ith member of the jth group, then our model for this situation is

$$x_{ij} = \mu + b_j + \varepsilon_{ij}$$

where b_j is the variation corresponding to membership of the jth group.

We use ANOVA to try to see whether these variations b_j are significant. The first step is to separate out the variations that come from the two different sources.

Within-group and between-group variation

Suppose we have a random variable X with a corresponding set of observations x_{ij} drawn from different groups within the population. Here, x_{ij} means the ith item from the jth group. We let $\bar{x}$ be the mean of the complete set of observations and $\bar{x}_j$ the mean of the jth group. Then we can express the difference between a particular observation x_{ij} and the total mean, i.e. $x_{ij} - \bar{x}$, as the sum of two separate differences by rewriting this as

$$x_{ij} - \bar{x} = (x_{ij} - \bar{x}_j) + (\bar{x}_j - \bar{x})$$

The first bracket is the difference between the item and the average of its particular group. This is called the *within-group* variation. The second bracket is the difference between this group mean and the overall mean. This is called the *between-group* variation.

As an example, we can let the random variable X be the time it takes me to get to work. I can take two possible routes, route A and route B. I note the time it takes on a number of occasions and come up with the following data.

	Route A		Route B			
	5		7			
	4		4			
	2		7		*Overall*	
	5		6			
Totals	16	$= T_A$	24	$= T_B$	40	$= G$
Means	4	$= \bar{x}_A$	6	$= \bar{x}_B$	5	$= \bar{x}$

We find the sums for each group and the total sum. From these, we can find the two group means and the overall mean.

Let's have a look at observation x_{32}, the third item in the second group. Looking at the table, we can see that this is 7. The difference between this observation and the overall mean is made up of two differences:

7 – 5	=	(7 – 6)	+	(6 – 5)
Difference of item from total mean		Difference of item from group mean		Difference of group mean from total mean
Total variation		*Within-group variation*		*Between-group variation*

since the overall mean is 5 and the group mean is 6 for route *B*.

Having isolated the two differences, we need a method for summing them so that we can see whether their relative totals are significant.

Sums of squares

In the case of $x_{32} - \bar{x}$ that we have just looked at, the differences both turned out to be positive. This is not always the case: $x_{23} - \bar{x}$ has negative between and within differences, for example. We then have the usual problem in dealing with sums of differences which can be both positive and negative: they cancel each other out, leaving no trace of the original observations. We avoid this by squaring the differences so that the result is always positive. These squares can then be added and the sum gives some idea of the original variations.

Usually when we square the sum of two terms we have to include the middle term, e.g. $(a + b)^2 = a^2 + 2ab + b^2$. In this case, however, when we square and add all the terms the middle term vanishes, leaving us with

$$\Sigma(x_{ij} - \bar{x})^2 = \Sigma(x_{ij} - \bar{x}_j + \bar{x}_j - \bar{x})^2$$
$$= \Sigma(x_{ij} - \bar{x}_j)^2 + \Sigma(\bar{x}_j - \bar{x})^2$$

where Σ means summing over all the *i*'s and *j*'s.

The proof of this can be found in more advanced statistics text-books if you are curious as to how this happens.

Total sum of squares	=	Within-group sum of squares	+	Between-group sum of squares

This can be written more briefly as

$$SS_T = SS_W + SS_B$$

We can verify this for the example of the journey times that we looked at before.

Total

Here, the overall mean is 5 and so the total sum of squares of the deviations from this is given by

$$SS_T = (5-5)^2 + (4-5)^2 + (2-5)^2 + (5-5)^2 + (7-5)^2 + (4-5)^2$$
$$+ (7-5)^2 + (6-5)^2$$
$$= 0 + 1 + 9 + 0 + 4 + 1 + 4 + 1 = 20 \qquad \qquad \text{...①}$$

Within

The mean for route A is 4: this gives the sum of squares within A as

$$(5-4)^2 + (4-4)^2 + (2-4)^2 + (5-4)^2 = 6$$

The mean for route B is 6: this gives the sum of squares within B as

$$(7-6)^2 + (4-6)^2 + (7-6)^2 + (6-6)^2 = 6$$

Altogether then, the within-group sum of squares is given by

$$SS_W = 6 + 6 = 12 \qquad \qquad \text{... ②}$$

Between

The square of the difference between group A and the overall mean is $(4-5)^2 = 1$. Each of the four items in group A has this variation, and so the between-group sum of squares is $4 \times 1 = 4$ for group A. Similarly, the between-group sum of squares is $4 \times (6-5)^2 = 4$ for group B. Altogether, the between-group sum of squares is given by

$$SS_B = 4 + 4 = 8 \qquad \qquad \text{... ③}$$

From ①, ② and ③, for this example, we have verified that

$$SS_T = SS_W + SS_B$$

Calculations

In the previous example, the figures were easy enough to manipulate and everything worked out very nicely. Data from a real-life population give figures that are not nearly so neat, and we need to simplify the calculations in order to reduce the working and the risk of error.

The method is basically the same as we used in the previous example. We sum each group, calling these sums $T_1, T_2, \ldots$ and add these sums to give the grand total G. From the group sums we can find the group means, $\bar{x}_1, \bar{x}_2, \ldots$ and from the grand total the overall mean, $\bar{x}$. We also need to square each item and find the sum of all these squares.

Total

Instead of $\Sigma(x_{ij} - \bar{x})^2$ we use the equivalent form

$$SS_T = \Sigma x_{ij}^2 - n\bar{x}^2$$
$$= \Sigma x_{ij}^2 - \frac{G^2}{n}$$

Between

If there are k groups and n items in the ith group, the computational formula for the between sum of squares is given by

$$SS_B = \frac{T_1^2}{n} + \frac{T_2^2}{n_2} + \dots + \frac{T_k^2}{n_k} - \frac{G^2}{n}$$

Within

We don't need to calculate the within sum of squares at all. We can rearrange $SS_T = SS_W + SS_B$ to give

$$SS_W = SS_T - SS_B$$

and so once we have found SS_T and S_B, we simply subtract them to find SS_W.

Returning to our example, we have $T_1 = 16$, $T_2 = 24$,

$$G = T_1 + T_2 = 16 + 24 = 40$$
$$n_1 = 4 \Rightarrow \bar{x}_1 = \frac{16}{4} = 4$$
$$n_2 = 4 \Rightarrow \bar{x}_2 = 6$$
$$n = n_1 + n_2 = 8 \Rightarrow \bar{x} = \frac{G}{n} = \frac{40}{8} = 5$$

Also, squaring each item and summing gives

$$\Sigma x_{ij}^2 = 5^2 + 4^2 + \dots + 6^2 + 7^2 = 220$$

We then calculate $SS_T = \Sigma x_{ij}^2 - \frac{G^2}{n} = 220 - \frac{40^2}{8} = 20$

$$SS_B = \frac{T_1^2}{n_1} + \frac{T_2^2}{n_2} - \frac{G^2}{n}$$
$$= \frac{16^2}{4} + \frac{24^2}{4} - \frac{40^2}{8} = 8$$
$$SS_W = SS_T - SS_B = 12$$

which are the values we found before.

Mean squares

One of the assumptions that is made in ANOVA is that the distribution underlying the population is normal. In this case we know that, using our total sum of squares, we can form an unbiased estimate s_T^2 for the population variance σ^2

$$s_T^2 = \Sigma \frac{(x_{ij} - \bar{x})^2}{n - 1}$$

We can also form a second unbiased estimate for σ^2 from the within sum of squares:

$$s_N^2 = \Sigma \frac{(x_{ij} - \bar{x}_j)^2}{n - k}$$

Both of these estimates hold regardless of whether the group means are the same. The third estimate is only true if there is no difference between the group means. It also relies on the second assumption that is made in ANOVA: that the variances between the samples are the same. In other words, even though the means may be different, the underlying variance of each group is the same. If these two conditions are met, then the estimate based on the between sum of squares,

$$s_B^2 = \Sigma \frac{(\bar{x}_j - \bar{x})^2}{k - 1}$$

is also an unbiased estimate for σ^2.

These unbiased estimates are called the *mean-squares*. We are now in a position to test the null hypothesis, which is that the means of all the groups are the same.

The *F*-test

We have formed one estimate for the population variance, s_W^2, which uses all the items in the calculation. The other estimate, s_B^2, uses only the group means in the calculation. If these are not equal this second estimate will be significantly higher than the first. Since they are both, by assumption, estimates for the same variance (and are in fact independent estimates) we can use the *F*-test on the ratio

$$\frac{\text{between mean-square}}{\text{within mean-square}}$$

The degrees of freedom correspond to the calculation of the mean-squares: $(k - 1)$ for between (k independent group means and 1 dependent mean) and $(n - k)$ for within (n independent items and k dependent means). If the ratio is greater than the critical value for the F-distribution with those degrees of freedom and the appropriate level of significance (usually 5%), we reject the null hypothesis and conclude that the means are not all the same.

As an example, we can calculate the ratio for the quantities we have found for the journey times.

Here, the between sum of squares was 8. There are only two groups and so $(2 - 1) = 1$ degree of freedom. This gives a between mean-square of $\frac{8}{1} = 8$.

The within sum of squares was 12. There are eight items and two group means, so $(8 - 2) = 6$ degrees of freedom. The within mean-square is $\frac{12}{6} = 2$

The F-ratio $= \dfrac{\text{between MS}}{\text{within MS}} = \dfrac{8}{2} = 4$

Looking at the 5% F-distribution with 1 and 6 degrees of freedom respectively, we find the value given as 5.99. Our F-ratio value of 4 is less than this critical value, so we conclude that the means are not significantly different at the 5% level.

Note that we are only interested in the case where the between MS is significantly greater than the within MS, so this test is always one-tailed.

Summary of procedure

The computational procedure for carrying out an ANOVA is

(i)   find the totals of each group, T_1, T_2 ...

(ii)   find the number in each group, n_1, n_2, ...

(iii)   find the grand total $G = T_1 + T_2 + ...$

(iv)   find the total number $n = n_1 + n_2 + ...$

(v)   square each item and find the sum of these squares

(vi)   calculate the total sum of squares $SS_T = \Sigma x_{ij}^2 - \dfrac{G^2}{n}$

(vii)   calculate the between sum of squares $SS_B = \dfrac{T_1^2}{n_1} + \dfrac{T_2^2}{n_2} + ... + \dfrac{T_k^2}{n_k} - \dfrac{G^2}{n}$

(viii)   find the within sum of squares by $SS_W = SS_T - SS_B$

(ix)   find the total degrees of freedom $df_T = n - 1$

(x)   find the between degrees of freedom $df_B = k - 1$

(xi)   subtract these for the within degrees of freedom $df_W = df_T - df_B$

(xii)   calculate the between MS $= \dfrac{\text{between sum of squares}}{df_B}$

(xiii)   calculate the within MS $= \dfrac{\text{within sum of squares}}{df_W}$

(xiv)   calculate the ratio of these, $F\text{-ratio} = \dfrac{\text{between MS}}{\text{within MS}}$

(xv)   find the critical F-value at the given level of significance, $F_{k-1,\,n-k}$

(xvi)   compare this with the calculated F-ratio

(xvii)   draw conclusions.

As with all hypothesis tests, you should state your null and alternative hypotheses before you start your analysis. It is also better to explain the implications of your conclusion rather than leaving it as '… so we reject the null-hypothesis'. Finally, the assumptions that need to be satisfied in order to use the ANOVA method are:

- that the items come from a normal distribution, and

- that each group has the same variance.

Here is an example which illustrates the procedure.

Example   In a hot, third-world country, milk is brought to the capital city from surrounding farms in churns carried on open lorries. The keeping quality of the milk is causing concern. The lorries could be covered to provide shade for the churns relatively cheaply or refrigerated lorries could be used but these are very expensive. The different methods were tried and the keeping quality measured. (The keeping quality is measured by testing the pH at frequent intervals and recording the time taken for the pH to fall by 0.5. A high value of this time is desirable.)

Keeping quality, hours		
Method of transport	Open	16.5, 20.0, 14.5, 13.0
	Covered	23.4, 25.0, 30.0, 33.5, 26.0
	Refrigerated	29.0, 34.0, 26.0, 22.5, 29.5, 30.5

(a)   Carry out a one-factor analysis of variance and test, at the 5% level, for differences between methods of transport.

(b)   Examine the method means and comment on their implications.

(c) Different farms have different breeds and different journey times to the capital, both of which could have affected the results. How could the data have been collected and analysed to allow for these differences?

[AEB 1992]

Solution   (a) We can rewrite the data in a table and add some of the quantities we will need in our calculations

		Total	Number	Mean
Open	16.5 20,0 14.5 13.0	$64 = T_1$	$4 = n_1$	16
Closed	23.5 25.0 30.0 33.5 26.0	$138 = T_2$	$5 = n_2$	27.60
Refrigerated	29.0 34.0 26.0 22.5 29.5 30.5	$171.5 = T_3$	$6 = n_3$	28.58
Total		$373.5 = G$	$15 = n$	24.9

We assume that the variance underlying each method is the same and that the data within each method are normally distributed.

We can now proceed to finding the sums of squares.

Between methods: $SS_M = \dfrac{T_1^2}{n_1} + \dfrac{T_2^2}{n_2} + \dfrac{T_3^2}{n_3} - \dfrac{G^2}{n}$

$$= \frac{64^2}{4} + \frac{138^2}{5} + \frac{171.5^2}{6} - \frac{373.5^2}{15}$$

$$= 434.692$$

$$= 434.7 \ (1 \text{ d.p.})$$

Total: $\quad SS_T = (\text{Sum of squares of all } n \text{ observations}) - \dfrac{G^2}{n}$

$$= 9906.75 - 9300.15$$

$$= 606.6$$

Within methods: $SS_W = SS_T - SS_M$

$$= 606.6 - 434.7$$

$$= 171.9$$

Now the degrees of freedom.

Between df $\ = (\text{Number of methods}) - 1$

$$= 3 - 1 = 2$$

Total df $= n - 1$

$\qquad = 15 - 1 = 14$

Within df $=$ total df – between df

$\qquad = 14 - 2 = 12$

We can now set up an ANOVA table to analyse the results, calculating our mean squares and F-ratio (to 1 d.p.):

Source	SS	df	MS	F-ratio
Between	434.7	2	217.4	15.2
Within	171.9	12	14.3	
Total	606.6	14		

The null hypothesis is that the means are the same, i.e. that the mean time is the same for each method:

$\quad$ H_0: $\mu_a = \mu_b = \mu_c$

The alternative hypothesis is that they are not equal:

$\quad$ H_1: μ_a, μ_b and μ_c are not all the same.

At the 5% level and with degrees of freedom 2 and 12 respectively, the F-value from the tables is 3.89.

Since our F-value of 15.2 is very much larger than this, we have a significant result and reject the null hypothesis. On the evidence of the given data we would say that, at the 5% level, the mean time is not the same for all the methods.

(b) Looking at the means, we see that the open lorries have a significantly lower time than either of the other two methods. These other two methods have very similar means: given that the relatively cheap method of transportation appears to give results comparable with the more expensive method, we might recommend that the lorries are merely covered, on the basis of these observations.

(c) We could have reduced the number of sources of variation by trying the different methods on one farm.

The alternative is to allow for an increased number of variables and carry out a two- or three-way ANOVA. This also tests whether different cattle or farms have an effect on the result.

In the previous example, the working was quite lengthy to include some explanation. The following example is probably closer to the solution you would give under exam conditions.

Example

The running costs of three different types of coal-fired central heating are to be compared. A coal merchant identifies 16 houses each with one of the three types of central heating. He records how much the occupier spends on coal between November and February.

		Expenditure on coal, £
	A	96, 49, 110, 146
Type of central heating	B	173, 67, 59, 94, 87, 142, 86
	C	210, 157, 53, 99, 194

Carry out a one-factor analysis of variance and test for differences in cost between types of central heating.

[AEB 1995]

Solution

Rewriting the data:

		Total	Number	Mean (2 d.p.)
A	96 49 110 146	$401 = T_1$	$4 = n_1$	100.25
B	173 67 59 94 87 142 86	$708 = T_2$	$7 = n_2$	101.14
C	210 157 53 99 194	$713 = T_3$	$5 = n_3$	142.60
Total		$1822 = T$	$16 = n$	113.88

Sums of squares

Between: $$SS_B = \frac{T_1^2}{n_1} + \frac{T_2^2}{n_2} + \frac{T_3^2}{n_3} - \frac{G^2}{n}$$

$$= 213483 - 207480$$

$$= 6003 \text{ (nearest whole number)}$$

Total: SS_T $$= (\text{sum of all squares}) - \frac{G^2}{n}$$

$$= 245892 - 207480$$

$$= 38412$$

179

Within: $SS_W = SS_T - SS_B$

$= 38412 - 6003$

$= 32409$

Our ANOVA table is

Source	SS	df	MS	F-ratio
Between	6003	2	3002	1.20
Within	32409	13	2493	
Total	38412	15		

$H_0: \mu_a = \mu_b = \mu_c$

$H_1: \mu_a, \mu_b$ and μ_c are not all the same.

At 5%, degrees of freedom 2 and 13 respectively, F-critical is 3.68.

Since the F-ratio is well below this, the result is not significant and we conclude that there is no reason to suppose that the different systems have different running costs, on the basis of the given observations.

Completely randomised design

We have been looking so far at cases where we have assumed that there is only one variable factor producing an effect on our response variable – the method of transport affecting keeping quality of milk, or the type of central heating affecting expenditure on coal. In order to carry out an experiment of this kind to test some hypothesis, we need first of all to decide how many observations are needed to make reasonably sure that if a difference in mean exists the test will prove to be significant. If we use too small a set of data the test becomes correspondingly less sensitive and real differences may escape detection. Having decided how many observations are required, we assign a portion at random to each level of the factor.

If there are only two levels, we could toss a coin, with heads representing level A and tails level B. Alternatively, we could look at a table of random numbers, perhaps assigning odd numbers to level A, even numbers to factor B until we had the required quota. With more than two levels of the factor, we could again use random number tables with a slight modification to the method. For instance, with three levels we could assign random two-digit numbers ending in 1, 2 or 3 to level A, ending in 4, 5 or 6 to level B and 7, 8, 9 to level C, ignoring any zeros. The exam questions you meet will frequently include different-sized samples for the various levels. In this way we can ensure a degree of randomisation in the chosen samples – it does mean, however, that some of the levels can be less well represented than others.

In other cases, it becomes obvious that there is more than one factor which has a significant effect on the response variable. In the next section we shall see how we can extend our method quite easily to analyse data from situations where we assume there are two such independent factors.

Two-way analysis of variance

We can imagine carrying out an experiment to see whether there was any difference in the time taken by several students carrying out a particular kind of task of standard difficulty: for example, adding columns of numbers in their heads. We can assume that they have practised sufficiently often that they are no longer noticeably improving. The times can be noted, giving the following results.

	Student				
	A	B	C	D	
	4	4	9	2	
	3	5	8	3	
	7	5	5	6	
Totals	14	14	22	11	61
	$= S_1$	$= S_2$	$= S_3$	$= S_4$	$= G$

(In this example, since the working is only for illustration, we have used fewer significant figures than usual.)

Carrying out a one-way ANOVA:

$$SS_T = \Sigma x_{ij}^2 - \frac{G^2}{n} = 359 - \frac{61^2}{12} = 48.92 \ (2 \text{ d.p.})$$

$$SS_B = \frac{S_1^2}{3} + \ldots + \frac{S_4^2}{3} - \frac{G^2}{n} = 22.25$$

$$SS_W = SS_T - SS_B = 26.67$$

Our table is

Source	SS	df	MS
Between	22.25	3	7.42
Within	26.67	8	3.33
Total	48.92	11	

This gives our test statistic

$$F = \frac{7.42}{3.33} = 2.2 \quad (1 \text{ d.p.})$$

Since the critical value of $F_{3,8}$ at the 5% level is 4.07, the result is not significant. We accept the null hypothesis: there is no evidence of any significant difference in the mean time taken by the students.

The reason that the F-ratio was low is that the within sum of squares is high. This means that overall there is such a large variation that even quite large differences between students are assumed to have happened by chance. In other words, the test is not very sensitive to differences between students.

We suspect that there is another factor acting which we have not accounted for, but which is producing the large variations. Returning to the original testing procedure, we find that some of the tests were taken in the morning, some at lunch-time and some in the afternoon. It could be that time of day has an effect on the time taken to complete the task. With this in mind, we rewrite the table with the results ordered according to the time of day:

		Student				
		A	B	C	D	
	Morning	4	4	5	2	$15 = T_1$
Time	Lunch	3	5	8	3	$19 = T_2$
	Afternoon	7	5	9	6	$27 = T_3$
		14	14	22	11	61
		$= S_1$	$= S_2$	$= S_3$	$= S_4$	$= G$

We carry out another ANOVA, but this time including in our analysis the results of the time-of-day factor. We hope this will reduce the sums of squares that arise from error and unknown factors, and thereby make the test more sensitive. Such an analysis is called a *two-way* ANOVA: the procedure is very much the same as for a one-way ANOVA except that we have two separate sums of squares for the factors we think may be affecting the time taken, i.e. $SS_{students}$ and $SS_{time of day}$.

Once we have found the total sum of squares and subtracted these two, the remainder is called the *residual sum of squares*. From this we can calculate the mean square of the residuals by dividing by the appropriate degrees of freedom. This mean square is then compared in turn with the mean square of the students and the mean square of the time of day. In this way, we carry out a pair of hypothesis tests using as before the resulting F-value of these ratios as our test statistic. The null hypotheses are then that there is no difference in means between students and no difference in means between time of day.

Here is the analysis of the data using a two-way ANOVA: the procedure is similar except that we find the 'between' sum of squares for the rows as well as the columns and subtract both these 'between' sums of squares from the total sum of squares.

$$SS_T \;=\; \Sigma x_{ij}^2 - \frac{G^2}{n} \qquad\qquad = 48.92 \quad \text{(as before)}$$

$$SS_{\text{students}} \;=\; \frac{s_1^2}{3} + \ldots + \frac{s_4^2}{3} - \frac{G^2}{n} \qquad = 22.25 \quad \text{(as before)}$$

$$SS_{\text{t-o-d}} \;=\; \frac{T_1^2}{4} + \frac{T_2^2}{4} + \frac{T_3^2}{4} - \frac{G^2}{n} \qquad = 18.67$$

$$
\begin{aligned}
SS_{\text{residual}} \;&=\; SS_T - \left[SS_{\text{students}} + SS_{\text{t-o-d}} \right] \\
&=\; 48.92 - [22.25 + 18.67] \\
&=\; 8.00
\end{aligned}
$$

The degrees of freedom are as before, except that now we have $3 - 1 = 2$ for the time of day. These are lost from the residual sum of squares: this makes the denominator of the residual mean-square smaller, which we don't really want since the smaller the mean-square, the more sensitive the test. The reduction in the residual sum-of-squares as a result of taking account of the additional factor should more than make up for this.

Students: our test statistic is $F \;=\; \dfrac{MS(\text{students})}{MS(\text{residual})} \;=\; \dfrac{7.42}{1.33} = 5.6$

Since the critical $F_{3,6}$–value at 5% is 4.76, this is a significant result and we reject the null hypothesis that the mean-time for all the students is the same. The evidence suggests that the students take differing mean-times.

Time of day: our test statistic is $F \;=\; \dfrac{MS(\text{time of day})}{MS(\text{residual})}$

$$= \frac{9.34}{1.33} = 7.0$$

The critical $F_{2,6}$-value at 5% is 5.14. Again, a significant result, leading us to reject the null hypothesis that the time of day has no effect on the time taken.

You can see that the reduction in the residual mean-square as a result of including the time-of-day factor in the analysis has meant that a previously not-significant test now becomes significant. In practice, of course, we would try and include this second factor from the start of the experiment.

Randomised block design

We saw in the section on experimental design in the previous module how, if we suspect that two separate factors are having an effect on the response variable, one factor can be blocked. Members of the group making up the other factor are then distributed randomly within each block in such a way that each member appears once in each block.

A typical example would be different varieties of a crop-vegetable as one factor and different plots of land as a possible secondary factor. Suppose we want to test four different varieties of the vegetable and we have divided the land into three different blocks. Within each block the secondary factor, e.g. drainage or sunlight, is more or less constant. The four different varieties are then distributed at random within the three blocks, giving, for example,

Block 1	A	D	C	B
Block 2	B	D	A	C
Block 3	D	A	B	C

The 12 plots are then planted with the vegetable and the response variable, typically the yield of the vegetable, is measured at the time of harvesting. This could give rise to the following situation.

Example Four varieties of potato are planted in three randomised blocks and the yields in kilograms per plot are as follows:

		Variety			
		A	*B*	*C*	*D*
	1	69	68	72	77
Block	2	72	73	76	79
	3	67	70	73	71

Carry out an analysis of variance and test for differences between blocks and between varieties.

We can code the data, using $Y = X - 70$, and sum the rows and columns

		Variety					
		A	B	C	D	Totals	
	1	−1	−2	2	7	6	$= B_1$
Block	2	2	3	6	9	20	$= B_2$
	3	−3	0	3	1	1	$= B_3$
	Totals	−2	1	11	17	27	
		$= V_1$	$= V_2$	$= V_3$	$= V_4$	$= G$	

Also, the total of the squares of each entry is

$$58 + 130 + 19 = 207$$

We can now find our sum of squares.

$$SS_T = \Sigma x_{ij}^2 - \frac{G^2}{n} = 207 - \frac{27^2}{12} = 146.25$$

$$SS_B = \frac{B_1^2 + B_2^2 + B_3^2}{4} - \frac{G^2}{n} = 48.50$$

$$SS_V = \frac{V_1^2 + V_2^2 + V_3^2 + V_4^2}{3} - \frac{G^2}{n} = 77.58$$

Using $SS_{\text{Residuals}} = SS_T - (SS_B + SS_V)$

We have $SS_R = 146.25 - (48.50 + 77.58)$

$$= 20.17$$

Degrees of freedom: $SS_T = 4 \times 3 - 1 = 11$

$$SS_B = 3 - 1 = 2$$

$$SS_V = 4 - 1 = 3$$

$$SS_R = 11 - (2 + 3) = 6$$

Our ANOVA two-way table becomes

Source	SS	df	MS
Blocks	48.50	2	24.25
Variety	77.58	3	25.86
Residual	20.17	6	3.36
Total	146.25	11	

185

Our test statistic for the blocks is

$$F = \frac{24.25}{3.36} = 7.22$$

At the 5% one-tailed, $F_{2,6} = 5.14$, i.e. significant

For the variety,

$$F = \frac{25.86}{3.36} = 7.70 \text{ and } F_{3,6} = 4.76, \text{ i.e. significant}$$

We reject the null hypothesis in both cases, and conclude that the evidence at the 5% level suggests differences between blocks, and also between varieties.

Summary of procedure

The computational procedure for carrying out a two-way $p \times q$ ANOVA is

(i)   find the totals of each row $R_1, R_2, \ldots R_p$

(ii)   find the totals of each column $C_1, C_2, \ldots C_q$

(iii)   find the grand total $G = \Sigma R_i = \Sigma C_i$

(iv)   calculate total number $n = p \times q$

(v)   square each item and find the sum of these squares

(vi)   calculate the total sum of squares $SS_T = \Sigma x_{ij}^2 - \dfrac{G^2}{n}$

(vii)   calculate the between rows SS, $SS_R = \displaystyle\sum_{i=1}^{p} \dfrac{R_i^2}{q} - \dfrac{G^2}{n}$

(viii) calculate the between columns SS, $SS_C = \displaystyle\sum_{i=1}^{q} \dfrac{C_i^2}{p} - \dfrac{G^2}{n}$

(ix)   calculate the residual SS, $SS_{Res} = SS_T - SS_R - SS_C$

(x)   find the total degrees of freedom, $df_T = n - 1$

(xi)   find the between rows df, $df_R = p - 1$

(xii)   find the between columns df, $df_C = q - 1$

(xiii) find the residual df, $df_{Res} = df_T - df_R - df_C$

(xiv)   calculate the between rows MS $= \dfrac{SS_R}{df_R}$

(xv)   calculate the between columns MS $= \dfrac{SS_C}{df_C}$

(xvi)   calculate the residual MS $= \dfrac{SS_{Res}}{df_{Res}}$

(xvii)   carry out F-test using $\dfrac{\text{Rows MS}}{\text{Residual MS}}$

(xviii)   carry out F-test using $\dfrac{\text{Columns MS}}{\text{Residual MS}}$

Assumptions and model

In the one-way ANOVA we assumed that only one factor was affecting the response variable, which was then modelled as

$$x_{ij} = \mu + b_j + \varepsilon_{ij}$$

By taking a randomly allotted number of readings for each group, we were able to estimate the overall variance. This process of taking a series of readings where everything is assumed constant is called *replication*. It helps us to form some idea of the inherent variation. We do not use it in our particular approach to two-way ANOVA. If we have m different varieties (or *levels*) of one factor and n levels of the other factor, we have just $m \times n$ cells in our table, with one observation in each cell. Each student is tested at each time of day, for example: we don't run a series of tests on one student at one particular time of day. This creates a slight problem: we can't form an idea of the inherent variation if everything is constant, because each observation is of a different combination of levels.

To simplify things, we make assumptions. In addition to the assumptions made for the one-way ANOVA, we assume that there is *no interaction between* the two factors. This means that none of the levels of one factor is biased either towards or against any of the levels of the other factor. On a practical level, this may not always be true. In our example of students and time of day it could well be that not all the students performed better in the morning: some might well feel better, and work quicker, later on in the day. Even so, we make this assumption. With this assumption, the residual sum of squares becomes our estimate for the overall variance, i.e. it performs the same task as our within sum of squares in one-way ANOVA.

The corresponding model under this assumption is

$$x_{ij} = \mu + s_i + t_j + \varepsilon_{ij}$$

where s_i and t_j are the variations corresponding to membership of the ith row and jth column respectively.

EXERCISES

Only a few have been included here: once you have mastered the general procedure, you will find further examples for practice in past examination papers (AEB Paper 10, pre-1996, Paper 6 afterwards, for example).

1 A physics teacher wished to investigate whether there was any significant difference in the results of three classes in Year 10. The data on test marks for the three classes are summarised in the table, using a coding of $x = \text{mark} - 50$.

Class	A	B	C	Total
Number of pupils, n	24	22	17	63
Σx	508	546	164	1218
Σx^2	13 106	14 967	10 056	38 129

(a) Test at the 5% level whether there are differences between the class means, stating the null and alternative hypotheses.

(b) State an assumption you have made about the distribution of the populations in order to carry out the test in part (a).

The teacher subsequently decided that she was interested in comparing the pupils in Class A with the other pupils.

(c) Describe briefly which testing method she should use, but do not perform the test.

[ULEAC 1996]

2 A factory is to introduce a new product which will be assembled from a number of components. Three different designs are considered and four employees are asked to compare their speed of assembly. The trial is carried out one morning. Each of the four employees assembled design A from 8.30 am to 9.30 am, design B from 10.00 am to 11.00 am and design C from 11.30 am to 12.30 pm. The number of products completed by each of the employees is shown in the following table:

Design	Employee			
	1	2	3	4
A	17	4	38	8
B	21	6	52	20
C	28	9	64	22

Carry out a two-factor analysis of variance and test at the 5% significance level for differences between designs and between employees. You may assume that the total sum of squares about the mean (SS_T) is 3878.9.

[AEB 1991]

3 Data were collected on the cost of repairs required in a one-year period for three types of central-heating boiler. Firm 1 was employed to repair one example of each of the three types, and Firm 2 was emloyed to repair another example of each of the three types. The cost of the repairs needed in £ is given in the table.

	Type *A*	Type *B*	Type *C*
Firm 1	12	15	6
Firm 2	60	45	30

(a) Copy and complete the following analysis of variance table.

Source	Degrees of freedom	Sum of squares	Mean square	Ratio
Firm				
Type		336		
Residual				
Total		2226		

(b) Test at the 5% level whether there is evidence of a difference between the firms, stating the null and alternative hypotheses.

[ULEAC, 1996]

4 (a) Twelve friends decided to slim. Each chose one of three alternative diets and recorded his or her weight loss at the end of one month.

Diet	*A*	*B*	*C*
	31	12	31
	23	54	70
	38	29	25
	54		51
			44

Carry out a one-factor analysis of variance and test at the 5% significance level whether there is a difference in weight loss between diets.

(b) It was pointed out that both the sex and the initial weight of the slimmer were likely to affect the amount of weight lost. A further trial was conducted in which only males took part and the participants were divided into three equal groups according to their initial weight. An analysis of the new trial led to the following table.

Source	Sum of squares	Degrees of freedom
Between diets	337	2
Between initial weights	649	2
Error	86	4
Total	1072	8

Test at the 5% significance level for differences between diets and between initial weights.

(c) Discuss why the two sets of data have led to different conclusions.

[AEB 1993]

5 Three brands of petrol were compared on five makes of car. The table below gives the kilometres travelled in each case, on a standard amount of petrol under similar conditions.

		Make of car				
		A	B	C	D	E
Brand	1	31.0	33.5	28.0	40.1	34.1
of	2	29.5	31.4	25.0	30.2	XXXX
petrol	3	22.7	32.1	26.4	29.8	30.1

Unfortunately, the observation intended for 'petrol' and 'car E' was found to be grossly in error due to a faulty instrument. No problems were encountered with any of the other observations, but for technical reasons an observation for 'petrol 2' and 'car E' could not be duplicated.

(a) Estimate this missing observation by the arithmetic mean of the other two observations for 'car E'.

(b) Now, assuming that this estimate is the actual observation for that cell, carry out the standard analysis of variance and test, at the 5% level of significance, for differences between makes of car and between brands of petrol.

[AEB 1979]

SUMMARY

When you have finished this section, you should

- know the model used in one-way ANOVA
- know the assumptions made in using one-way ANOVA
- be familiar with the terms: sum of squares and mean-squares
- know how to calculate the appropriate degrees of freedom
- be familiar with, and know how to carry out, the procedure for a one-way ANOVA
- appreciate the connection between completely randomised design and one-way ANOVA
- know how to apply randomised block design to two-way ANOVA
- be familiar with, and know how to carry out, the procedure for a two-way ANOVA
- be familiar with the terms: residuals, levels, factors
- know the assumptions made in two-way ANOVA

Projects

You will already have completed one project for your work in T2 and have a good idea of the structure and procedure that is necessary. You may find it helpful to re-read the comprehensive section in *Statistics 2* on projects. This section adds some brief ideas which you could find useful. It suggests a sequence of stages you will probably have to go through in carrying out your project.

Purpose

There are a number of reasons for doing the project, some easier to define than others. Amongst these are:

● *Context*: In carrying out the project, you should gain a good idea of the subject as a whole and where your particular bit fits in.

● *Practicality*: The effect of actually using statistics instead of studying it can be quite an eye-opener: rather like studying French and then going to Paris and seeing that what you learnt actually works and has a purpose.

● *Guaranteed marks*: On a more pragmatic level, you're doing it because once you have completed it, you will have put so many marks in the bank, so to speak. It can be quite a comfort to think that you only need so many more marks to get your 'A' level: the exam can then become slightly less nerve-wracking.

● *Competence*: You will find that you are more confident in your ability to answer questions in the exam relating to the area of the syllabus you have included in your project.

Having put yourself into a positive frame of mind for tackling your project, you can start the planning, beginning with your choice of topic.

Topic

Ideally, you will find something that you are interested in investigating, either because it's a hobby of yours or because it ties in with some other work you're doing. In this case, you're much more likely to make an effort to go to a library, for example, and read further if necessary, or ask for explanation of some part of the theory.

You can find some ideas for projects in the section in *Statistics 2* or you may have some other resources. Whatever you choose, discuss with your tutor what it might entail and whether it is suitable. Remember also that your examining board can give advice on this if you approach it through your centre.

Aim

Having decided on your general area, you will need to narrow this down to a very specific target. Something like 'I want to see whether product A is better than product B' is not precise enough. It has to be something more along the lines of 'I want to see whether product A lasts longer, performs more effectively, yields a greater weight (or whatever) than product B.' With a clear objective, planning the experiment will be easier.

Design

You should be familiar with the elements of experimental design that were talked about in T3. Included in these are:

- *response variable*: how you are going to define and measure the quantity you're interested in

- *sample size*: how large a sample you need to take

- *analysis:* you must be able to analyse the data you collect, so the project must lend itself to appropriate analysis

- *available techniques*: you should have some idea of which additional techniques are available to you now you have studied T3/T4. These include *t*-tests, analysis of variance, *F*-tests etc. They will form the basis of your analysis of the data

- *data collection*: which specific methods are necessary for the various techniques – e.g. paired or unpaired samples for a *t*-test

- *assumptions*: each technique makes various assumptions. You will have to make sure you list these and state which tests or precautions you have taken to ensure that the conditions are satisfied

- *target population*: you will need to define this carefully and show that you took steps to ensure that any sample taken was a *random* sample

- *bias*: you will probably need to select a sample using a process of randomisation to reduce the possibility of bias. Make sure you include a description of your method of selecting and assigning your sample. It will probably involve using random number tables.

Other points may occur to you. Whatever they are, make sure you include them in your report so that the examiner can see that you carried out your project in a thoughtful and resourceful manner. You might, for example, make a little trial run before your main experiment to see whether there is some fault that you didn't anticipate in your design.

Data

You will already be familiar with collecting and recording data, and the attendant difficulties, from your earlier project. Make sure you make a note of any little point or refinement that you may have to make in this stage and include it in your report

Analysis

Include in the analysis a clear statement of the null and alternative hypotheses, assumptions, justifications and critical values. Make your working as clear and concise as possible: your data, for example, could be briefly summarised while the raw data could be included elsewhere, possibly in an appendix.

Presentation

You should aim to make the project look neat and professional: data carefully arranged, graphs clearly drawn and labelled. The topics in T3/T4 do not lend themselves so readily to graphic presentation as those in T1/T2, but, if possible, try and find a way of summarising your conclusions in some kind of visual manner.

Conclusions

You should make it clear how your project has investigated the problem you stated in the beginning and the conclusions you have come to in the light of the data and corresponding analysis. Whether or not you have reached any definite conclusion is not at all the main point. The important point is that you show that you have approached the project with the right attitude, that you have made reasonable attempts to plan the procedure and overcome any difficulty, and that you have analysed your experimental data efficiently and accurately.

Here are a couple of further ideas to finish this section.

Timing

Give yourself plenty of time. This will:

- allow you to avoid the 'Oh my goodness, I've got to hand in my project in a fortnight's time and I haven't even started it yet' syndrome. This is stressful for you and those around you.

- increase your chance of putting together a well-planned, coherent project that will earn you good marks. This will also be something that you keep and feel quite proud of.

- mean that the time that you need to set aside for the project will be spread over a longer period. You won't then end up resenting spending a lot of your spare time on it.

Outside resources

You may decide that you have access to the equipment which will allow you to carry out an experiment with the appropriate degree of accuracy and rigour. On the other hand, you may decide that you haven't the necessary resources. In this case, you might consider contacting some reputable outside concern that uses statistics and may even employ professional statisticians. Write a polite letter, saying that you are a student who has to carry out a project – would it be possible to know the kinds of project they carry out in their business, how the data are collected and analysed etc. You might even ask whether you could be included in some project – in this way you would be part of something practical and you would have some interesting data to analyse that you would never have been able to collect on your own. You would naturally still have to complete the project yourself and make sure that you clear the whole thing with your teacher/tutor/parents.

The following are some examples of concerns which use statistics.

- *supermarkets*: How do they decide which products are grouped together? How do they decide on their pricing policy, which products to reduce for a while? How do they decide how long to stay open and how many people to employ on the tills?

- *consumer magazines*: How do they plan and conduct their surveys? How many people do they ask? How do they avoid bias?

- *examination boards*: You will actually find that the boards are a good source of secondary data, with the percentages of passes at the various levels in each subject published in their annual reports.

- *manufacturers*: How do they decide what packaging to use, what price to charge, what name to call the product? How do they control the flow of stock to their outlets? What advertising should they use? What is the response from adverts on the television, in the newspapers, as a mail-shot?

- *university research departments*: They will certainly have some projects on the go. They research into nutrition, psychology, geography, physiology… If you are considering applying to a university it might give you some idea of the areas that are researched and the methods used. Many students have to use statistics in their courses.

- *traffic planning departments*: How do they decide where to put traffic lights? How long should each branch be given a green light? Does this change in the course of a day? How long are the respective queues that form on the different branches?

The list could go on and on but you can probably work out for yourself where you might approach if you decide to try this line. Remember also that you probably have an additional resource already – your other subject tutors. They may well be able to suggest a project that would help you in their subject as well as in statistics.

Good luck and enjoy it!

Section 1

1

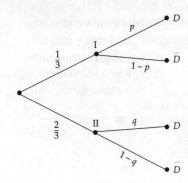

$$P(I \mid D) = \frac{\frac{1}{3}p}{\frac{1}{3}p + \frac{2}{3}q} = \frac{p}{p + 2q}$$

2 Given

$P(A)$ = 0.35
$P(B)$ = 0.25
$P(C)$ = 0.40
$P(D \mid A)$ = 0.03
$P(D \mid B)$ = 0.06
$P(D \mid C)$ = 0.05

(a) (i) $P(A \cap D) = P(D \mid A \ P(A)$
$$= (0.03)(0.35) = 0.0105$$

(ii) $P(D) = P(A \cap D) + P(B \cap D)$
$$+ P(C \cap D)$$
$$= P(D \mid A) P(A) + P(D \mid B) P(B)$$
$$+ P(D \mid C) P(C)$$
$$= (0.03)(0.35) + (0.06)(0.25)$$
$$+ (0.05)(0.40)$$
$$= 0.0455$$

(b) $P(C \mid D) = \dfrac{P(D \mid C) P(C)}{P(D)}$
$$= \frac{(0.05)(0.40)}{0.0455}$$
$$= 0.4396 \ (4 \text{ d.p.})$$

(c) $P(A \mid \bar{D}) + P(B \mid \bar{D})$

$$= \frac{P(A \cap \bar{D})}{P(\bar{D})} + \frac{P(B \cap \bar{D})}{p(\bar{D})}$$

$$= \frac{(0.35)(0.97) + (0.25)(0.94)}{1 - 0.0455}$$

$$= 0.6019 \ (4 \text{ d.p.})$$

3 (a) (i) $P(S) = \dfrac{72}{200} = \dfrac{9}{25}$

(ii) $P(R \cap S) = \dfrac{18}{200} = \dfrac{9}{100}$

(iii) $P(\bar{T} \cup \bar{S}) = \dfrac{178}{200} = \dfrac{89}{100}$

(iv) $P(S \mid R) = \dfrac{P(S \cap R)}{P(R)} = \dfrac{\frac{18}{200}}{\frac{50}{200}} = \dfrac{9}{25}$

(b) $\overline{R \cup T}$ (or $\bar{R} \cap \bar{T}$)

(c) (i) T. Bicycle can't be both touring
and racing
(ii) S and R as from (a) $P(S \mid R) = P(S)$
(iii) T as calculation gives $P(S \mid T)$

$$= \tfrac{11}{35} \neq P(S)$$

(d) (i) Blue racing = 5
Blue touring = 28
Blue mountain = 16
$$P(\text{Blue}) = \tfrac{49}{200}$$

(ii) $P(M \mid B) = \dfrac{P(M \cap B)}{P(B)} = \dfrac{16}{49}$

4 (a) $P(A \cup B) = P(A) + P(B) - P(A \cap B)$
$$\Rightarrow P(A \cap B) = 0.32 + 0.5 - 0.55 = 0.27$$

(b) $P(\bar{A} \mid B) = \dfrac{P(\bar{A} \cap B)}{P(B)}$

$$= \frac{P(B) - P(A \cap B)}{P(B)}$$

$$= \frac{0.23}{0.5} = 0.46$$

(c) $P(A \mid \bar{B}) = \dfrac{P(A \cap \bar{B})}{P(\bar{B})}$

$$= \frac{P(A) - P(A \cap B)}{P(\bar{B})} = \frac{0.05}{0.5} = 0.1$$

5 Given $P(A \cap B) = P(A)\,P(B)$

$\therefore\ P(A) + P(B) - P(A \cup B) = P(A)\,P(B)$

$\Rightarrow 1 - P(\bar{A}) + 1 - P(\bar{B}) - P(A \cup B)$

$= (1 - P(\bar{A}))\,(1 - P(\bar{B}))$

$\Rightarrow 1 - P(\bar{A}) + 1 - P(\bar{B}) - P(A \cup B)$

$= 1 - P(\bar{A}) - P(\bar{B}) + P(\bar{A})\,P(\bar{B})$

$\Rightarrow 1 - P(A \cup B) = P(\bar{A})\,P(\bar{B})$

$\Rightarrow\ P(\overline{A \cup B}) = P(\bar{A})P(\bar{B})$

$\Rightarrow\ P(\bar{A} \cap \bar{B}) = P(\bar{A})\,P(\bar{B})$

$\Rightarrow \bar{A}$ and $\bar{B}$ are independen.t

6 (a) Possible scores are

1, 2, 3, 4, 5, 6 (white only)

2, 3, 4, 5, 6, 7, 8, 9, 10, 11, 12 (both dice)

giving:

r	1	2	3	4	5	6
$P(X = r)$	$\frac{6}{72}$	$\frac{7}{72}$	$\frac{8}{72}$	$\frac{9}{72}$	$\frac{10}{72}$	$\frac{11}{72}$

r	7	8	9	10	11	12
$P(X = r)$	$\frac{6}{72}$	$\frac{5}{72}$	$\frac{4}{72}$	$\frac{3}{72}$	$\frac{2}{72}$	$\frac{1}{72}$

$P(3 \le X \le 7) = \dfrac{8}{72} + \dfrac{9}{72} + \dfrac{10}{72} + \dfrac{11}{72} + \dfrac{6}{72}$

$$= \frac{44}{72} = \frac{11}{18}$$

We assume that the dice are also fair.

(b) (i) $\dfrac{32}{200} = \dfrac{4}{25}$

(ii) $\dfrac{100}{200} = \dfrac{1}{2}$

(iii) $\dfrac{62}{100} = \dfrac{31}{50}$

$P(W \cup G) = \dfrac{188}{200}$ $P((W \cup G) \cap S) = \dfrac{94}{200}$

Also $P((W \cup G))P(S) = \dfrac{188}{200} \times \dfrac{1}{2} = \dfrac{94}{200}$

$\therefore\ P((W \cup G))P(S) = P((W \cup G) \cap S)$

$\therefore$ independent.

Taking W = white, S = saloon as an illustration (any other combination will do)

$P(W) = \dfrac{130}{200}$ $P(S) = \dfrac{1}{2}$

$P(W \cap S) = \dfrac{68}{200}$ and $P(W)P(S) = \dfrac{65}{200}$

$\therefore\ P(W)\,P(S) \ne P(W \cap S)$

$\Rightarrow W, S$ are dependent events.

7 Write G = Verdict of 'guilty'

NG = Verdict of 'not guilty'

NP = Verdict of 'not proven'

I = Accused is innocent

We are given:

$P(G)$	= 0.75
$P(NG)$	= 0.15
$P(NP)$	= 0.10
$P(I \mid G)$	= 0.06
$P(I \mid NG)$	= 0.93
$P(I \mid NP)$	= 0.30

(a) Using the theorem of total probability

$P(I) = P(I \mid G)\,P(G) + P(I \mid NG)\,P(NG)$
$\quad + P(I \mid NP)\,P(NP)$

$= (0.06)\,(0.75) + (0.93)\,(0.15)$
$\quad + (0.30)\,(0.10)$

$= 0.2145$

(b) $P(G \mid I) = \dfrac{P(I \mid G)\,P(G)}{P(I)}$

$= \dfrac{(0.06)\,(0.75)}{0.2145}$

$= 0.2098$ (4 d.p.)

Although only approximately one in five people is wrongly brought to trial (result (a)) it is also the case that approximately one fifth of guilty verdicts are recorded for people who are innocent.

8 Given $P(D) = \dfrac{1}{500} = 0.002$

$P(\text{Pos} \mid D) = 0.98$

$P(\text{Pos} \mid \bar{D}) = 0.03$

(a) $P(\text{Pos}) = P(\text{Pos} \mid D)\,P(D)$

$\quad + P(\text{Pos} \mid \bar{D})\,P(\bar{D})$

$= (0.98)\,(0.002) + (0.03)\,(0.998)$

$= 0.0319 = 3.19\%$

(b) $P(D \mid \text{Pos}) = \dfrac{P(\text{Pos} \mid D)\, P(D)}{P(\text{Pos})}$

$\quad = \dfrac{(0.98)\,(0.002)}{0.0319}$

$\quad = 0.0614 = 6.14\%$ (3 sig. figs.)

Only approximately 6% giving a positive result have the disease. Clearly a follow-up test would be required.

(c) $P(D \mid \overline{\text{Pos}}) = \dfrac{P(\overline{\text{Pos}} \mid D)\, P(D)}{P(\overline{\text{Pos}})}$

$\quad = \dfrac{0.02 \times 0.002}{1 - 0.0319}$

$\quad = 0.00004132$ (4 sig. figs.)

9 Let A = 'knows the answer'

$\phantom{\text{Let }} \overline{A}$ = 'guesses the answer'

$\phantom{\text{Let }} C$ = 'answers question correctly'

We require $P(A \mid C)$.

Using Bayes' theorem

$P(A \mid C) =$

$$\dfrac{P(A)\, P(C \mid A)}{P(A)\, P(C \mid A) + P(\overline{A})\, P(C \mid \overline{A})}$$

$= \dfrac{p \,.\, 1}{p \,.\, 1 + (1 - p)\,.\,\dfrac{1}{5}}$

$= \dfrac{5p}{4p + 1}$

When $P = \dfrac{1}{6}$, $p(A \mid C) = \dfrac{1}{2}$

so even when the probability of him actually knowing the answer is as low as $\dfrac{1}{6}$ we can be 50% sure that if he answers correctly he actually knew rather than guessed the answer.

Section 2

1 $\Sigma x_i = 167.6$

$ \Sigma x_i^2 = 3561.28$

$ n = 8$

$\Rightarrow \overline{x} = \dfrac{167.6}{8} = 20.95$

$ s^2 = \dfrac{8}{7}\left(\dfrac{3561.28}{8} - 438.9025\right)$

$ = 7.1514$

$H_0: \mu = 21.5$

$H_1: \mu < 21.5$

5% significance

$t = \dfrac{20.95 - 21.5}{2.674/\sqrt{8}} \sim t_7$

$\Rightarrow t = -0.5818$

Critical value $= -1.895$

Accept H_0.

2 $H_0: \mu = 30$

$ H_1: \mu \neq 30$

5% significance

$\Sigma x_i = 359.4$

$\Sigma x_i^2 = 10791.96$

$n = 12$

$\Rightarrow \overline{x} = 29.95$

$ s^2 = \dfrac{12}{11}\left(\dfrac{10791.96}{12} - 29.95^2\right)$

$ = 2.5391$

$t = \dfrac{29.95 - 30}{1.5935/\sqrt{12}} \sim t_{11}$

$\Rightarrow t = -0.1087$

Critical value $= -2.201$

Accept H_0.

3 $\Sigma x_i = 757.1$

$ \Sigma x_i^2 = 57349.47$

$ n = 10$

$\Rightarrow \overline{x} = 75.71$

$ s^2 = \dfrac{10}{9}\left(\dfrac{57349.47}{10} - 75.71^2\right)$

$ = 3.2699$

98% interval is

$$75.71 \pm (2.821) \left(\frac{1.8083}{\sqrt{10}}\right)$$

$$= 75.71 \pm 1.613$$
$$= (74.10, 77.32) \text{ (to 2 d.p.)}$$

4 $H_0: \mu = 74$

$H_1: \mu > 74$

5% significance

$$t = \frac{75.71 - 74}{(1.8083/\sqrt{10})} \sim t_9$$

$$\Rightarrow \quad t = 2.9904$$

Critical value from tables is 1.833

Reject H_0.

5 $H_0: \sigma^2 = 36$

$H_1: \sigma^2 < 36$

Test statistic $= \dfrac{14 \times 25.2}{36} = 9.8$

From tables, critical value is 6.571

Accept H_0.

To reject H_0 would require a value of s^2

where $\dfrac{14s^2}{36} < 6.571$

$\Rightarrow s^2 < 16.90$ (2 d.p.)

6 $\Sigma x_i = 1935.9$

$\Sigma x_i^2 = 275547.81$

$n = 14$

$\Rightarrow \bar{x} = 138.2786$

$$s^2 = \frac{14}{13}\left(\frac{275547.81}{14} - 19120.9633\right)$$

$$= 604.1787$$

(i) For $\chi^2(13)$ the % points are
5.009 and 24.736

Hence $P\left(5.009 < \dfrac{(13)(604.1787)}{\sigma^2} < 24.736\right)$

$= 0.95$

$\Rightarrow P\left(\dfrac{(13)(604.1787)}{24.736} < \sigma^2 < \dfrac{(13)(604.1787)}{5.009}\right)$

$= 0.95$

giving the interval
(317.5, 1568.0)

(ii) 95% interval is

$$138.2786 \pm (2.160)\left(\frac{24.58}{\sqrt{14}}\right)$$

i.e. 138.2786 ± 14.19

i.e. $(124.1, 152.5)$

(iii) 95% interval is

$$138.2786 \pm (1.96)\left(\frac{17}{\sqrt{14}}\right)$$

i.e. 138.2786 ± 8.905

i.e. $(129.4, 147.2)$

Comment

In the light of the interval obtained in (i), the population variance of 289 assumed in (iii) is very dubious since it lies outside 95% CI. Hence the interval obtained in (ii) is more appropriate.

7 (a) 95% interval is, using $\dfrac{9s^2}{\sigma^2} \sim \chi^2(9)$

$$2.700 < \frac{(9)(0.83)}{\sigma^2} < 19.023$$

$$\Rightarrow \quad 0.393 < \sigma^2 < 2.767$$

$$\Rightarrow \quad 0.63 < \sigma < 1.66$$

(b) $H_0: \mu = 20$

$H_1: \mu > 20$

5% significance

$$t = \frac{20.6 - 20}{0.911/\sqrt{10}} \sim t_9$$

$$\Rightarrow \quad t = 2.083$$

Critical value is 1.833

Reject H_0 (diameter has increased) on evidence of sample.

(c) (i) $D \sim N(20, \sigma^2)$

(ii) $D \sim N(\mu, \sigma^2)$ for some $\mu > 20$

8 (a) A Type I error is made when we incorrectly reject H_0 and a Type II error is made when we incorrectly accept H_0.

(i) The size of a test is
α = the significance level of the test.

(ii) The power of a test is $1 - \beta$ where β is the probability of making a Type II error.

(b) A: $N(500, 5.3^2)$

B: $N(504, 4.8^2)$

H_0: Batch from A ($\mu = 500$)

H_1: Batch from B ($\mu > 500$)

5% significance level (since we require $\alpha = 0.05$)

Reject H_0 if $\bar{x} > k$

where under H_0, $\bar{X} \sim N\left(500, \frac{5.3^2}{6}\right)$

i.e.　　find k from

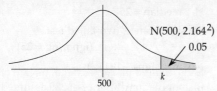

$N(500, 2.164^2)$

0.05

500

k

$P\left(Z > \frac{k - 500}{2.164}\right) = 0.05$

$\Rightarrow k = 503.6$

A type II error will occur if we wrongly accept H_0. This will occur if we obtain a value for $\bar{x} < 503.6$

when $\bar{X} \sim N\left(504, \frac{4.8^2}{6}\right)$.

The probability of this is 0.411.

(c) Calculation gives $\bar{x} = 501.67$ and since $501.67 < 503.6$ we accept H_0.

(d) $n = 25$, so 19 more boxes.

9 (a) $P(X \le 2)$ for $X \sim P(6)$

is　$e^{-6} + 6e^{-6} + \frac{6^2}{2}e^{-6}$

　　$= 25e^{-6}$

　　$= 0.0620$

(b) $\beta = P(X \ge 3)$ where $\mu < 6$

　　$= 1 - P(X \le 2)$

　　$= 1 - \left(e^{-\mu} + \mu e^{-\mu} + \frac{\mu^2}{2}e^{-\mu}\right)$

$\Rightarrow 1 - \beta$ (the power function)

　　$= e^{-\mu} + \mu e^{-\mu} + \frac{\mu^2}{2}e^{-\mu}$

　　$= \frac{e^{-\mu}}{2}\left(2 + 2\mu + \mu^2\right)$

(c) $s = \frac{1}{2}e^{-2}(2 + 4 + 4)$

　　$= 5e^{-2} = 0.68$

$t = \frac{1}{2}e^{-5}(2 + 10 + 25)$

　　$= \frac{37}{2}e^{-5} = 0.12$

(d)

Power

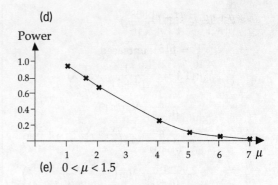

1.0 –
0.8 –
0.6 –
0.4 –
0.2 –

1　2　3　4　5　6　7　μ

(e) $0 < \mu < 1.5$

10 (a) A consistent estimator, $\hat{\theta}$, of a parameter θ is one for which $\mathrm{Var}(\hat{\theta}) \to 0$ as $n \to \infty$.

(b) $T_1 = \frac{\bar{X} + \bar{Y}}{2}$

$\Rightarrow E(T_1) = \frac{1}{2}E(\bar{X}) + \frac{1}{2}E(\bar{Y})$

　　　　　$= \frac{1}{2}\mu + \frac{1}{2}\mu = \mu$

$\mathrm{Var}(T_1) = \frac{1}{4}\mathrm{Var}(\bar{X}) + \frac{1}{4}\mathrm{Var}(\bar{Y})$

　　　　　$= \frac{1}{4}\mathrm{Var}\left(\frac{X_1 + X_2 + \ldots + X_{10}}{10}\right)$

　　　　　$+ \frac{1}{4}\mathrm{Var}\left(\frac{Y_1 + Y_2 + \ldots Y_n}{n}\right)$

　　　　　$= \frac{1}{400}\left(\sigma^2 + \sigma^2 + \ldots + \sigma^2\right)$

　　　　　$+ \frac{1}{4n^2}\left(\sigma^2 + \sigma^2 + \ldots + \sigma^2\right)$

　　　　　$= \frac{1}{400}\left(10\sigma^2\right) + \frac{1}{4n^2}\left(n\sigma^2\right)$

　　　　　$= \frac{\sigma^2}{40} + \frac{\sigma^2}{4n}$

　　　　　$= \frac{\sigma^2}{40}\left(1 + \frac{10}{n}\right)$

Hence T_1 is unbiased since $E(T_1) = \mu$

T_1 is not consistent since $\mathrm{Var}(T_1)$

$\to \frac{\sigma^2}{40}$ as $n \to \infty$

(ii) $E(T_2) = \left(\frac{1}{n+1}\right)E(\bar{X}) + \left(\frac{n}{n+1}\right)E(\bar{Y})$

　　　　$= \frac{1}{n+1}\mu + \frac{n}{n+1}\mu$

$$= \frac{\mu + n\mu}{n + 1} = \frac{(1 + n)}{1 + n}\mu$$

$$= \mu \Rightarrow \text{unbiased}$$

$$\text{Var}(T_2) = \frac{1}{(n + 1)^2} \text{Var}(\bar{X})$$

$$+ \frac{1}{(n + 1)^2} \text{Var}(n\bar{Y})$$

$$= \frac{1}{(n + 1)^2} \text{Var}\left(\frac{X_1 + X_2 + \ldots + X_{10}}{10}\right)$$

$$+ \frac{n^2}{(n + 1)^2} \text{Var}\left(\frac{Y_1 + Y_2 + \ldots + Y_n}{n}\right)$$

$$= \frac{1}{100(n + 1)^2}(10\sigma^2) + \frac{1}{(n + 1)^2} n\sigma^2$$

$$= \frac{\sigma^2}{10(n + 1)^2} + \frac{n\sigma^2}{(n + 1)^2}$$

$$= \frac{(1 + 10n)}{10(n + 1)^2} \sigma^2 \to 0 \text{ as } n \to \infty$$

$$\Rightarrow \text{consistent}$$

(iii) $\dfrac{10\bar{X} + n\bar{Y}}{10 + n}$ is such an estimator

(a 'weighted' average).

Section 3

1 H_0: median = 25

H_1: median $\neq$ 25

5% significance, two-tailed test

$+ - - + + + + - + + +$ (ignoring = 25)

No. of + signs $\sim B(11, \tfrac{1}{2})$

$P(X \geq 11) = \left(\tfrac{1}{2}\right)^{11} = 0.0005$

$P(X \geq 10) = 11\left(\tfrac{1}{2}\right)^{10}\left(\tfrac{1}{2}\right)^1 + 0.0005 = 0.0059$

$P(X \geq 9) = 55\left(\tfrac{1}{2}\right)^9\left(\tfrac{1}{2}\right)^2 + 0.0059 = 0.0327$

Critical region is $X \geq 10$ or $X \leq 1$

$X = 8 \Rightarrow$ accept H_0

2 Differences (Proposal 2 – Proposal 1)

$+ + - + + + + + - - +$

H_0: no difference

H_1: proposal 2 is better than Proposal 1 (one-tailed)

5% significance

$+$ signs $\sim B\left(11, \tfrac{1}{2}\right)$

$P(X = 11) = \left(\tfrac{1}{2}\right)^{11} = 0.0005$

$P(X \geq 10) = 0.0059$

$P(X \geq 9) = 0.0328$

$P(X \geq 8) = 165\left(\tfrac{1}{2}\right)^8\left(\tfrac{1}{2}\right)^3 + 0.0328$

$= 0.1133$

Critical region is $X \geq 9$.

$X = 8 \Rightarrow$ accept H_0 (no difference)

3 H_0: median = 25

H_1: median $\neq$ 25 (two-tailed)

5% significance

Difference	3.2	–3.5	–0.4	0.3	4.1	2.4	...
Rank	8	9	4	3	11	6	...

Difference	1.2	–0.2	0	3.7	6.4	3.1	...
Rank	5	2	1	10	12	7	...

$S^+ = 8 + 3 + 11 + 6 + 5 + 1 + 10 + 12 + 7$

$= 63$

$S^- = 9 + 4 + 2 = 15$

$S = 15$

From tables (p. 233) under $n = 12$ at column 0.025 we find the critical value 13.

Since $S(\text{calc}) > S(\text{tab})$ we accept H_0.

4 Table of differences (Maths – Physics)

Difference	11	1	−6	−10	−4	22	...
Rank	9	1	5	8	3	10	...

Difference	2	−7	8	−5
Rank	2	6	7	4

$S^+ = 9 + 1 + 10 + 2 + 7 = 29$
$S^- = 5 + 8 + 3 + 6 + 4 = 26$
$\Rightarrow S = 26$

H_0: no difference

H_1: median scores are different (two-tailed)

5% significance

From table on p. 234 under sample size $n = 10$ and 0.025 (since two-tailed) we find the value of 8.

Since $S(\text{calc}) > S(\text{tab})$ we accept H_0.

No evidence of a difference.

5 $S \sim N(\dfrac{(10)\,(11)}{4}, \dfrac{(10)\,(11)\,(21)}{24})$

$\sim N(27.5, 96.25)$

$z = \dfrac{(26 + 0.5) - 27.5}{\sqrt{96.251}} = -0.1019$

which is well within the acceptance region for H_0. (i.e. $-1.96 \rightarrow 1.96$).

6 Combined data:

Time	0	60	90	120	150	180	190
Rank	1	2	3	4	5	6	7

Time	200	210	220	240	280	285	290
Rank	8	9	10	11	12	13	14

Time	300	320	350	420	520
Rank	15	16	17	18	19

$T = 1 + 2 + 6 + 8 + 9 + 11 + 13 + 17 + 18$
$= 85$

H_0: the samples come from a population with the same median value

H_1: medians are different (two-tailed)

5% significance

$n_1 = 9, n_2 = 10$

From tables we have a value of 65.

Since $T(\text{calc}) > T(\text{tab})$ we accept H_0.

7 (a) The data are discrete and we are testing median values.

(b) H_0: medians are the same for class A and class B

H_1: $\text{median}_A \neq \text{median}_B$

5% significance

Combined data	8	10	11	12	13	15
Rank	1	2	3	4	5	6

Combined data	16	17	18	20	22
Rank	7	8	9	10	11

$T = 1 + 2 + 3 + 5 + 7 = 18$

$n_1 = 5, n_2 = 6$

Tables give 18.

Since $T(\text{calc}) \leq T(\text{tab})$ we reject H_0.

There is a difference in the medians at the 5% significance level.

(c) Normal approximation is required

$T \sim N\left(\dfrac{(25)\,(51)}{2}, \dfrac{(25)\,(25)\,(51)}{12}\right)$

$\sim N(637.5, 2656.25)$

$z = \dfrac{522.5 - 637.5}{\sqrt{2656.25}} = -2.23$

This value is in the critical region for a two-tailed test at 5% level so we reject H_0. There is a difference in the medians of the classes.

Section 4

1 $n = 10$, $\Sigma x_i = 204$, $\Sigma y_i = -49.69$,

$\Sigma x_i^2 = 4584$, $\Sigma y_i^2 = 289.6749$,

$\Sigma x_i y_i = -1148.06$

leading to

$$S_{xx} = 4584 - \frac{204^2}{10} = 422.4$$

$$S_{yy} = 289.6749 - \frac{(-49.69)^2}{10} = 42.7653$$

$$S_{xy} = -1148.06 - \frac{(204)(-49.69)}{10}$$

$$= -134.384$$

$$\hat{\beta} = \frac{-134.384}{422.4} = -0.3181$$

$$\hat{\alpha} = \left(\frac{-49.69}{10}\right) - \left(\frac{204}{10}\right)(-0.3181)$$

$$= 1.5211$$

x_i	y_i	$\hat{\alpha} + \hat{\beta}x_i$	ε_i	ε_i^2
10	−1.62	−1.6599	0.0399	0.0016
12	−2.29	−2.2961	0.0061	0.0000
14	−3.01	−2.9323	−0.0777	0.0060
18	−4.21	−4.2047	−0.0053	0.0000
20	−4.79	−4.8409	0.0509	0.0026
22	−5.49	−5.4771	−0.0129	0.0002
24	−6.13	−6.1133	−0.0167	0.0003
26	−6.73	−6.7495	0.0195	0.0004
28	−7.41	−7.3857	−0.0243	0.0006
30	−8.01	−8.0219	0.0119	0.0001
			−0.0086	0.0118

$$\text{RSS} = S_{yy} - \frac{(S_{xy})^2}{S_{xx}}$$

$$= 42.7653 - \frac{(-134.384)^2}{422.4}$$

$$= 0.0118$$

The estimate of σ^2 is given by

$$s^2 = \frac{0.0118}{8} = 0.0015$$

$$\Rightarrow s = 0.0384$$

Comment: All the ε_i apart from one are well within $2s$ of the mean.

2 (a)

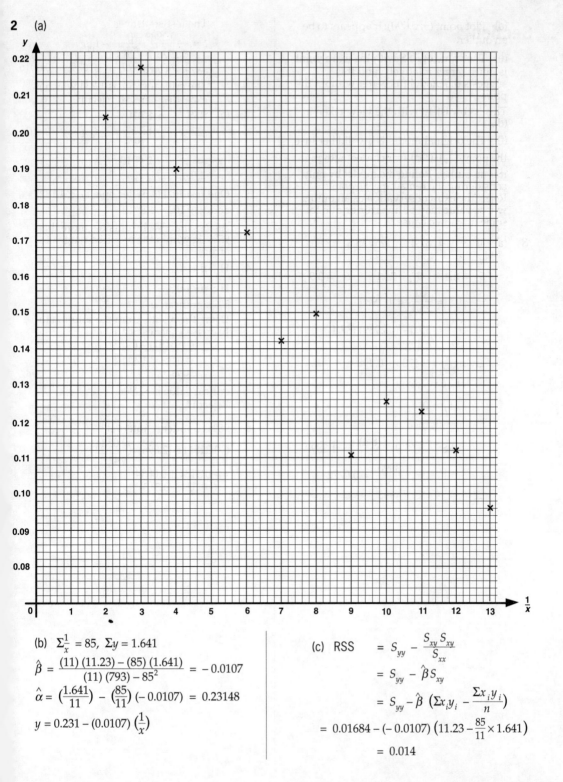

(b) $\Sigma\frac{1}{x} = 85, \ \Sigma y = 1.641$

$\hat{\beta} = \dfrac{(11)\,(11.23) - (85)\,(1.641)}{(11)\,(793) - 85^2} = -0.0107$

$\hat{\alpha} = \left(\dfrac{1.641}{11}\right) - \left(\dfrac{85}{11}\right)(-0.0107) = 0.23148$

$y = 0.231 - (0.0107)\left(\dfrac{1}{x}\right)$

(c) RSS $= S_{yy} - \dfrac{S_{xy}\,S_{xy}}{S_{xx}}$

$= S_{yy} - \hat{\beta}S_{xy}$

$= S_{yy} - \hat{\beta}\left(\Sigma x_i y_i - \dfrac{\Sigma x_i y_i}{n}\right)$

$= 0.01684 - (-0.0107)\left(11.23 - \dfrac{85}{11}\times 1.641\right)$

$= 0.014$

(d)   Plot point (5, 0.090); it appears to be an outlier.

(e)   The value of RSS with the extra point is much larger relatively, and this suggests the model fits better without the point.
This is consistent with the view taken in (d).

(f)   The original model is invalid because the point $\left(\frac{1}{5}, 0.090\right)$ is included, although it is an outlier. Refine the model by only considering the remaining 11 points. Reject the extra observation as an outlier whose value may be an error or due to some unknown cause.

3   (a) (i) $\bar{x}$ = 87.4 $\bar{y}$ = 35.6

$n = 20$

$S_{xy} = 8.4$ $S_{xx} = 28.1$ $S_{yy} = 3.9$

$\Rightarrow \hat{\beta}$ $= \dfrac{8.4}{28.1} = 0.2989$

$\hat{\alpha}$ = 35.6 − (0.2989) (87.4)

  = 9.4733

giving $y = 9.4733 + 0.2989x$

(ii) $H_0: \hat{\beta} = 0$

$H_1: \hat{\beta} > 0$

5% significance

RSS $= 3.9 - \dfrac{(8.4)^2}{28.1} = 1.3890$

s^2 $= \dfrac{1.3890}{18} = 0.0772$

$\Rightarrow$ s = 0.2778

The test-statistic is

$t = \dfrac{0.2989 - 0}{0.2778 \,/\, \sqrt{28.1}} \sim t_{18}$

$\Rightarrow t = 5.7036$

The critical value is 1.734 which is exceeded here, so reject H_0.

(b)   RSS = 83.10

$\Rightarrow s^2$ $= \dfrac{83.10}{19} = 4.3737$

$\Rightarrow s$ = 2.0913

$\Rightarrow 2s$ = 4.1827

One residual (4.5) lies outside ± 4.1827 and $\frac{1}{21} \times 100 = 4.8\%$

As less than 5% lie outside, more than 95% lie within the required range of errors.

4 $H_0: \beta = -0.3$

$H_1: \beta \neq -0.3$

5% significance

Using the results from the solution to Exercise 1 the test statistic

t $= \dfrac{(-0.3181) - (-0.3)}{0.0384 \,/\, \sqrt{422.4}}$

   = −9.6874 ~ t_8

critical value is −2.306.
Reject H_0.

5   98% confidence interval is

$(-0.3181) \pm (2.896) \left(\dfrac{0.0384}{\sqrt{422.4}}\right)$

= −0.3181 ± 0.0054
= (−0.324, −0.313)

Section 5

1 Note: These solutions are by no means exhaustive. There are many other valid points you could have mentioned.

(a) We have to state assumptions

Generally, that

- variables are normally distributed
- each factor has the same variance
- effects are additive.

(b) Has to be large enough to make result potentially significant.

For comparison, sample sizes should be approximately equal.

(c) Also called residual error.

The variation that remains after the variation due to known factors has been removed.

Includes inherent variation, together with effect of unknown factors.

Idea is to minimise the experimental error. This makes the test more sensitive.

(d) Repeat experiment under identical conditions as far as possible.

Gives an idea of inherent variation.

(e) Has to be clearly defined.

Has to be relevant and useful.

Has to be measurable in a reasonably objective way.

(f) Used to distribute effect of known and unknown factors. Avoids bias on part of subject and/or experimenter.

Necessary for normal distribution assumptions.

Avoids large variation due to a systematic factor.

Once framework has been decided, factors allotted at random.

(g) Area where some factor *A* is constant.

Subdivided so that each level of factor *B* occurs somewhere within constant area.

(h) Levels of factor *B* distributed at random within each block of factor *A*.

Eliminates or reduces systematic effects.

(i) Design where each row and each column contains all levels of a particular factor, efficient for time and money.

Possibly too many assumptions for simplification to be justified.

Tables available for all possible squares for any number.

Particular square chosen at random.

Rows and columns allotted at random.

Variable factors allotted at random.

2 They could be improving their performance if designs are similar. If the designs are too similar this could confuse operators. Could tire, or lose initial enthusiasm to do well.

Need to mix these effects up, since difficult to assess. Each employee given the order of designs chosen at random.

3 Need to standardise more.

Response variable should include time heating is working, particularly since period includes Christmas and holidays. Need to know whether people at home or away, since major effect from this. Need to know the cost of different sources and the age of the central heating systems. Amount of coal used per house would be a better response variable – further complications from the temperature at which people keep their houses, how many rooms, etc.

4 *Data collection*: will all the possible data be collected? No – many people will not bother to note time and inform shopkeeper. If not, do the data form a random sample from the entire possible collection? No – doesn't include people who haven't yet had punctures; biased towards short time until puncture.

Response variable: not well defined. 'Performance' of a tyre, length of time it lasts is what you want to know, but how to measure this? Doesn't take into account terrain, amount of use, weight of rider. Could be punctured from faulty spoke, i.e. inside, not outside.

Sample sizes: should be more nearly equal, since assuming normal distributions.

Design: Assumption of normal distribution questionable: variance too large, too much probability of outliers, e.g. very large time if bike little used, etc. Too much variance from unknown factors, attempts should be made to pair the tyres, e.g. by fitting at random one to front and other to back of bike.

5 Could be a systematic factor from the type of patient who first asks for painkiller.

Response variable extremely subjective and possibly dependent on time of day: e.g. pain felt worse at night, maybe not so bad when something to do during the day.

Wouldn't expect variance to be the same for very severe and mild.

Given the relatively short time effective, would need several times a day. Could design an experiment where the same patient takes each of the four brands. Consider blocking for time of day, i.e. run the experiment over four days, so that each painkiller tested over each period in day. This would remove much of the subjective variation. Need professional experience to decide whether the severity of the pain should be included. If so, would need to standardise type of patient with regard to various factors.

Section 6

1   95% at $25 \pm (1.9600) \left(\frac{0.4}{\sqrt{9}}\right)$

98% at $25 \pm (2.3263) \left(\frac{0.4}{\sqrt{9}}\right)$

95% at 24.739 and 25.261

98% at 24.690 and 25.310

2   (a)   98% lines at $12 \pm (2.3263) \left(\frac{0.35}{\sqrt{10}}\right)$

99% lines at $12 \pm (2.5758) \left(\frac{0.35}{\sqrt{10}}\right)$

98% at 11.743 and 12.257

99% at 11.715 and 12.285

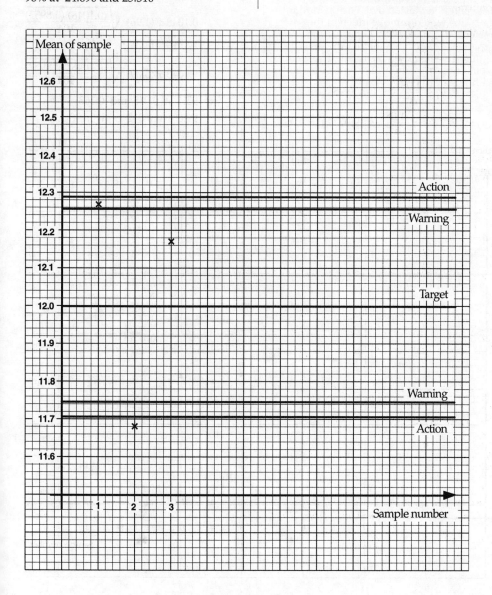

(b) The first sample suggests that another sample should be taken as soon as possible.

A second sample suggests that adjustments to machinery should be made.

The third sample suggests that the operation is now working smoothly but another sample should be taken to confirm.

(c) $(n-1)\dfrac{s^2}{\sigma^2} \sim \chi^2(n-1)$

$\Rightarrow 9 \times \dfrac{0.12}{\sigma^2} \sim \chi_9^2$

$\Rightarrow P\!\left(x_1 \le \dfrac{1.08}{\sigma^2} \le x_2\right) = 0.95$

$\Rightarrow P\!\left(2.700 \le \dfrac{1.08}{\sigma^2} \le 19.0232\right) = 0.95$

$\Rightarrow P\!\left(\dfrac{1.08}{19.023} \le \sigma^2 \le \dfrac{1.08}{2.700}\right) = 0.95$

giving 95% C.I. of $(0.057, 0.400)$

3   (a) $p = \dfrac{109}{1040} = 0.1048$ (4 d.p.)

Average $n = \dfrac{1040}{10} = 104$

95% lines at

$0.1048 \pm (1.96)\sqrt{\dfrac{(0.1048)\,(0.8952)}{104}}$

99.8% lines at

$0.1048 \pm (3.09)\sqrt{\dfrac{(0.1048)\,(0.8952)}{104}}$

$\Rightarrow$ 95% at 0.045 and 0.163

99.8% at 0.012 and 0.198

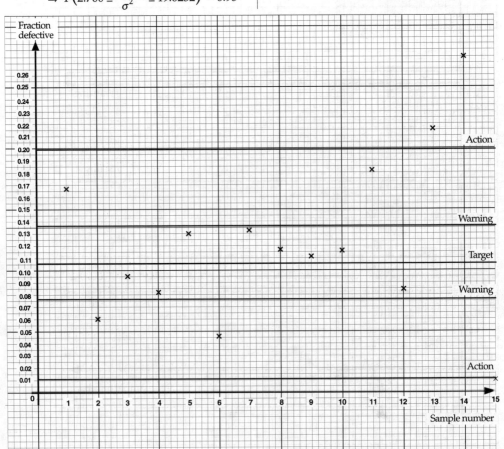

(b)   Comments

(i) $p = 0.183$ No action needed but immediate resample

(ii) $p = 0.085$ No action necessary

(iii) $p = 0.217$ Action necessary and immediate resample

(iv) $p = 0.25$ Further action necessary plus increase sample size

(v) $p = 0.010$ Process has responded to the action.

4   (a) $p = \dfrac{131}{800} = 0.16375$

1 in 40 above or below warning $\Rightarrow$ 95% limits

1 in 1000 above or below action $\Rightarrow$ 99.8% limits

95% limits at

$$0.16375 \pm (1.96)\sqrt{\frac{(0.16375)\,(0.83625)}{80}}$$

99.8% limits

$$0.16375 \pm (3.09)\sqrt{\frac{(0.16375)\,(0.83625)}{80}}$$

95% at 0.245 and 0.081
99.8% at 0.292 and 0.036

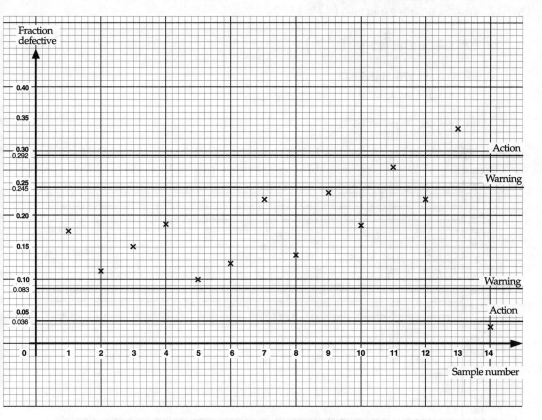

(b)

0.275   Between warning and action: suggests another sample should be taken immediately if possible.

0.225   Within bounds

0.3375   Action should be taken

0.025   No action necessary. p has decreased, possibly as a result of previous action taken.

(c) $n = 80$ and $p = 0.32$

so the number of unsatisfactory deliveries, $X \sim B(80, 0.32)$

For this distribution we require
$P(X > 80 \times 0.292)$

$= P(X > 23.36)$

i.e. $P(X \geq 24)$ since X is discrete.

Using the normal approximation (with continuity correction) we have

$X \sim N(25,6, 17.408)$

and require $P(X > 23.5)$

$= P\left(Z > \dfrac{23.5-25.6}{\sqrt{17.408}}\right)$

$= P(Z > 0.5033)$

$= 0.6927$

---

5 (a) (i) 95% lines at $2.0 \pm (1.96)\left(\dfrac{0.042}{\sqrt{9}}\right)$

        99% lines at $2.0 \pm (2.5758)\left(\dfrac{0.042}{\sqrt{9}}\right)$

      $\Rightarrow$ 95% at 1.973 and 2.027

      99% at 1.964 and 2.036

(ii)

Mean of sample

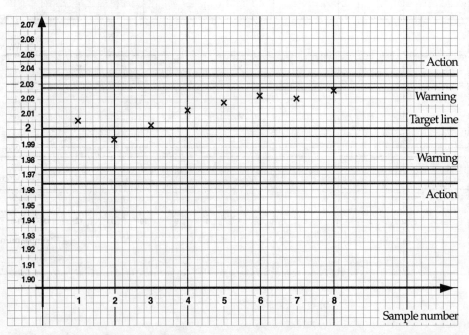

(iii) The pattern suggests that the process is progressively heading out of control and that frequent samples should be taken to see if this is confirmed. If the upward trend continues over the next few samples then adjustments should be made to reduce the amount of powder dispensed. After adjustment, frequent samples should be taken to make sure the operation is now working correctly.

(b) *Method A*

X = number of defective cartons

$X \sim B(50, 0.02)$

probability of accepting batch = $P(X \leq 2)$

$= (0.98)^{50} + 50(0.98)^{49}(0.02) + 1225(0.98)^{48}(0.02)^2$

$= 0.9216$

Method B

Probability of accepting batch =

$(0.98)^{40} + 40(0.98)^{39}(0.02)(0.98)^{40} + 40(0.98)^{39}(0.02). 4(0.98)^{39}(0.02)$

$\begin{Bmatrix} \text{no defectives in} \\ \text{1st sample} \end{Bmatrix}$ or $\begin{Bmatrix} \text{1 defective} \\ \text{in 1st sample} \end{Bmatrix} \begin{Bmatrix} \text{no defectives} \\ \text{in 2nd sample} \end{Bmatrix}$ or $\begin{Bmatrix} \text{1 defective} \\ \text{in 1st sample} \end{Bmatrix} \begin{Bmatrix} \text{1 defective} \\ \text{in 2nd sample} \end{Bmatrix}$

$= 0.7402$

---

6 (a) *Method A*

$X \sim B(10, p)$

$p(X \leq 2) = (1-p)^{10} + 10(1-p)^9 p + 45(1-p)^8 p^2$

$= (1-p)^8 [(1-p)^2 + 10p(1-p) + 45p^2]$

$= (1-p)^8 [36p^2 + 8p + 1]$

Method B

Accept sample with probability

$(1-p)^5 + 5p(1-p)^4 (1-p)^5 + 5p(1-p)^4 5p(1-p)^4$

$\begin{Bmatrix} \text{no defectives in} \\ \text{1st sample} \end{Bmatrix}$ or $\begin{Bmatrix} \text{1 defective} \\ \text{in 1st sample} \end{Bmatrix} \begin{Bmatrix} \text{no defectives} \\ \text{in 2nd sample} \end{Bmatrix}$ or $\begin{Bmatrix} \text{1 defective} \\ \text{in 1st sample} \end{Bmatrix} \begin{Bmatrix} \text{1 defective} \\ \text{in 2nd sample} \end{Bmatrix}$

$= (1-p)^5 [1 + 5p(1-p)^4 + 25p^2(1-p)^3]$

(b) *Method A* $p = 0.2$ gives 0.6778

    $p = 0.5$ gives 0.0547

   Method B $p = 0.2$ gives 0.6297

    $p = 0.5$ gives 0.0605

(c) For low probability of defectives we are more likely to accept using Method A. For high probability of defectives the difference between the two methods is minimal. Hence A is better.

---

7 *Plan 1*

X = number of defectives

$X \sim B(50, 0.05)$

$P(X \leq 3) = 1 - P(X \geq 4)$

$= 1 - 0.2396$ (from table)

$= 0.7604$

Plan 2

Accept batch if:

sample 1 has not more than 1 defective with probability $1 - 0.4465$ (from table)

$= 0.5535$

or

sample 1 has two defectives and sample 2 has no defectives with probability

$(0.4465 - 0.1878)(1.0000 - 0.7854)$

$= 0.0555$

sample 1 has two defectives and sample 2 has one defective with probability

$(0.4465 - 0.1878)(0.7854 - 0.4465)$

$= 0.0877$

(d) Sample 1 has two defectives and sample 2 has two defectives with probability

$(0.4465 - 0.1878)^2$

$= 0.0669$

⇒ Accept with probability 0.5535 + 0.0555 + 0.0877 + 0.0669 = 0.764

showing that the probabilities are approximately the same.

If $p = 0$ then there would be no defectives in the first sample of 30 so we would just sample 30 items.

If $p = 0.02$ we would sample 30 items if for $X \sim B(30, 0.02)$ we have $X \le 1$, but we would sample 60 items if for $X \sim B(30, 0.02)$ we have $X = 2$. Hence the expected number sampled

$$= 30[(0.98)^{30} + \binom{30}{1}(0.98)^{29}(0.02)]$$

$$+ 60[\binom{30}{2}(0.98)^{28}(0.02)^2]$$

$$= 32.31 \quad (2 \text{ d.p.})$$

If $p = 0.05$ the calculation, by similar reasoning, is

$$= 30((0.95)^{30} + \binom{30}{1}(0.95)^{29}(0.05))$$

$$+ 60[\binom{30}{2}(0.95)^{28}(0.05)^2]$$

$$= 32.12 \quad (2 \text{ d.p.})$$

If $p = 0.10$ we have

$$= 30[(0.9)^{30} + \binom{30}{1}(0.9)^{29}(0.1)]$$

$$+ 60(\binom{30}{2}(0.9)^{28}(0.1)^2)$$

$$= 19.17 \quad (2 \text{ d.p.})$$

If $p = 1.00$ we would reject after sampling the first batch so the expected number sampled = 30.

We have

p	0.00	0.02	0.05	0.10	1.00
E(items inspected)	30	32.31	32.12	19.17	30

giving the graph

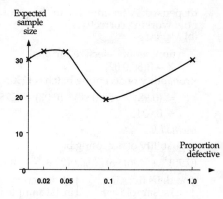

Plan 1 is simpler to use, but you would expect on average to have to sample more items – use Plan 1 if sampling is cheap and simple to operate.

Plan 2 inspects fewer items on average and so this one is preferable where sampling is expensive or difficult.

8 (a) Number of defectives $X \sim B(10, p)$

Accept if $X \le 2$

$$P(X \le 2) = (1 - p)^{10} + 10(1 - p) + 45p^2(1 - p)^8$$

$$= (1 - p)^8 \left[(1 - p)^2 + 10p(1 - p) + 45p^2\right]$$

$$= (1 - p)^8 \left[1 + 8p + 36p^2\right]$$

(b) Expected number of hinges inspected

$$= 10(1 - p)^8 (36p^2 + 8p + 1)$$

$$+ 200 \left[1 - (1 - p)^8 (36p^2 + 8p + 1)\right]$$

$$= 200 - 190(1 - p)^8(36p^2 + 8p + 1)$$

$p = 0.1$	gives	23.3
$p = 0.2$	gives	71.2
$p = 0.3$	gives	127.3

Where the proportion of defectives is high this scheme would be very costly.

T4

Solutions

Section 7

1 $(0.6)^2 \times 0.4 = 0.144$

$E(X) = \dfrac{1}{p} = \dfrac{1}{\frac{2}{5}} = \dfrac{5}{2} = 2.5$

2 $(0.96)^4 \times 0.04 = 0.034$ (3 d.p.)

3 (i) Geometric with $p = 0.278$

(ii) $P(R = 3) = (0.722)^2 \times 0.278 = 0.145$

(iii) $E(R) = \dfrac{1}{p} = 3.60$ (3 sig.figs.)

$\mathrm{Var}(R) = \dfrac{q}{p^2} = 9.34$ (3 sig.figs.)

4 (i) $\left(\frac{1}{2}\right)^4 \times \frac{1}{2} = \dfrac{1}{32}$

(ii) Either $HHHHT$ or $TTTTH = 2 \times \dfrac{1}{32}$
$= \dfrac{1}{16}$

5 Assuming that the occurrence of one faulty item is independent of another (i.e. no 'bunching' due to machine or operator deterioration), a geometric distribution would be a suitable model.

(i) $P(X \geq 3) = q^2 = (0.88)^2 = 0.77$ (2 d.p.)

(ii) $E(X) = \dfrac{1}{p} = \dfrac{1}{0.12} = 8\frac{1}{3}$

6 There needs to be a series of independent trials, with two possible outcomes 'success' and 'failure'. The probability of a success has to be constant. Then if X is the number of trials up to and including the first success, X has a geometric distribution with the given probability function.

$\begin{aligned} P(X \leq r) &= 1 - P(X > r) \\ &= 1 - P \text{ (first } r \text{ trials all 'failures')} \\ &= 1 - (1 - p)^r \end{aligned}$

$P(X > s + t \mid X > s) = P\dfrac{(X > s + t \cap X > s)}{P(X > s)}$

$= \dfrac{(X > s + t)}{P(X > s)}$

$= \dfrac{(1 - p)^{s+t}}{(1 - p)^s} = (1 - p)^t$

$= P(X > t)$

This means that however long you wait, the probability of having to wait a further time t is the same as having to wait a time t when you started, i.e. the probability is independent of the time you have already waited. This is known as the loss of memory property.

$P(X = 30) = 0.9^{29} \times 0.1 = 0.0047$ (2 sig.figs.)

Need $P(X \leq r) > 0.9 \Rightarrow 1 - q^r > 0.9$

$\Rightarrow q^r < 0.1$

$q = 0.9 \Rightarrow 0.9^r < 0.1 \Rightarrow r > \dfrac{\log 0.1}{\log 0.9} = 21.9$

Since r is an integer, $r = 22$, and the man books his holiday on December 22nd.

7 The proof of the first part is in the last example in the text.

For someone to win in one particular trial, there must be either one head and $(n - 1)$ tails or one tail and $(n - 1)$ heads. The total probability for these is

$2 \times {}^nC_1 \left(\frac{1}{2}\right)^n = 2 \times \dfrac{n}{2^n}$ since ${}^nC_1 = n$

$= \dfrac{n}{2^{n-1}}$

This is in fact p.

So $P(X = r) = \dfrac{n}{2^{n-1}} \left(1 - \dfrac{n}{2^{n-1}}\right)^{r-1}$

For a geometric distribution, $E(X) = \dfrac{1}{p} = \dfrac{2^{n-1}}{n}$

We saw before that

$\begin{aligned} P(X \leq k) &= 1 - P(X > k) \\ &= 1 - P \text{ [failing first } k \text{ times]} \\ &= 1 - q^k \end{aligned}$

With $n = 7$, $p = \dfrac{7}{2^6} = \dfrac{7}{64} \Rightarrow q = 1 - p = \dfrac{57}{64}$

We need $1 - \left(\frac{57}{64}\right)^k > 0.5$

$\Rightarrow \left(\frac{57}{64}\right)^k < 0.5 \Rightarrow k > \dfrac{\log 0.5}{\log\left(\frac{57}{64}\right)}$

$\qquad\qquad\qquad = 5.98$

Since k is an integer, $k \geq 6$

8 We can model this situation by a negative binomial distribution, since the trials are independent and there is a constant probability of success, $p = 0.1$.

(a) If X is the number of days she phones in until she has been allowed to speak three times,

$P(X = n) = \binom{n-1}{k-1}p^k q^{n-k}$

$\qquad = \binom{n-1}{3-1}(0.1)^3 (0.9)^{n-3}$, $n = 3, 4, \ldots$

(b) $P(X = 21) = \binom{20}{2}0.1^3\, 0.9^{17} = 0.032$
(2 sig.figs.)

(c) Unlikely: radio person will recognise voice and will either be irritated (less chance) or pleased (more chance). In any case, not independent.

9 (i) Using a negative binomial model, with $p = 0.3$

(i) $P(X = 7) = \binom{7-1}{3-1}(0.3)^3 (0.7)^4$

$\qquad\qquad = 0.097$ (2 sig.figs.)

(ii) $E(X) = \dfrac{k}{p} = \dfrac{3}{0.3} = 10$

$\qquad \text{Var}(X) = \dfrac{kq}{p^2} = \dfrac{3 \times 0.7}{0.3^2} = 23\frac{1}{3}$

10 (a) $\dfrac{P(X = x)}{P(X = x-1)} = \dfrac{(x-1)!}{(n-1)!\,(x-n)!}$

$p^n q^{x-n} \times \dfrac{(n-1)!\,(x-n-1)!}{(x-2)!}\;\dfrac{1}{p^n q^{x-n-1}}$

$= \dfrac{(x-1)\,q}{(x-n)}$

since $\dfrac{(x-1)!}{(x-2)!} = x-1$, etc,

$\left(\text{e.g. } \frac{8!}{7!} = 8\right)$

We want $\quad P(X = x) > P(X = x-1)$

i.e. $\dfrac{P(X = x)}{P(X = x-1)} > 1 \qquad \dfrac{(x-1)q}{x-n} > 1$

$\Rightarrow (x-1)q > x-n \quad (x \geq n+1)$

$\qquad xq - q > x - n$

$\qquad n - q > x - xq$

$n - q > x(1 - q) = xp$

i.e. $x < \dfrac{n-q}{p}$

Reversing these steps gives the required result.

(b) Here $p = 0.12$, $n = 6$

From the first part, if $x < \dfrac{n-q}{p} = \dfrac{6 - 0.88}{0.12}$

i.e. if $x \leq 42$, then $P(X = x) > P(X = x-1)$, the most likely number is 42

$\Big($As a check,

$P(X = 41) = \binom{40}{5}(0.12)^6 (0.88)^{34} = 0.02545$

$P(X = 42) = \ldots = 0.02551$

$P(X = 43) = \ldots = 0.02548\Big)$

11 The cumulative distribution function for X is

$F(x) = P(X \leq x) = 1 - e^{-\lambda x}$, $x > 0$

$\qquad\qquad = 1 - e^{-\frac{x}{10}}$ with $\lambda = \dfrac{1}{10}$

$\Rightarrow F(2) = P(X \leq 2) = 1 - e^{-0.2} = 0.18127$

$\quad F(5) = P(X \leq 5) = 1 - e^{-0.5} = 0.39347$

$\quad F(15) = P(X \leq 15) = 1 - e^{-1.5} = 0.77687$

$\Rightarrow X \leq 2 \qquad F(2) = 0.18127 \quad$ 8 points

$2 < X \leq 5 \;\; F(5) - F(2) = 0.21220 \quad$ 5 points

$5 < X \leq 15 \;\; F(15) - F(5) = 0.38340 \quad$ 1 point

$E(X) = 8 \times 0.18127 + 5 \times 0.21220 + 1 \times 0.38340$

$\qquad = 1.45016 + 1.0610 + 0.38340$

$\qquad = 2.89456 \Rightarrow E(X) = 2.895$ (3 d.p.)

12 We have to be careful of units.

In one minute, you expect $\dfrac{7.2}{5} = 1.44$ customers.

$\Rightarrow$ CDF for the time is

$P(X \leq x) = 1 - e^{-1.44x}$ where x is time in mins.

(a) When $x = \frac{1}{2}$, $P\left(X \leq \frac{1}{2}\right) = 1 - e^{-0.72} = 0.513$ (3 d.p.)

(b) Independent arrivals, $x = 1$, $P(X \leq 1) = 1 - e^{-1.44} = 0.763$

$P(X \leq 2) = 1 - e^{-2.88} = 0.944$

$\Rightarrow P(1 \leq X \leq 2) = 0.944 - 0.763 = 0.181$ (3 d.p.)

13 Expect $\frac{3}{2}$ calls in 60 secs = 1 min

$\Rightarrow \lambda = \frac{3}{2}$

and PDF is $f(x) = \frac{3}{2}e^{-\frac{3}{2}x}$, $x > 0$

$\qquad\qquad = 0, \quad x \le 0$

$\text{CDF} = \int_0^x f(x)\,dx = \left(e^{-\frac{3}{2}x}\right)_0^x$

$\qquad\qquad\qquad = 1 - e^{-\frac{3}{2}x}, x > 0$

$\qquad\qquad\qquad = 0 \quad \text{elsewhere}$

We need $P(2 \le X \le 3)$, where X is waiting time for next call.

$F(3) - F(2) = \left(1 - e^{-\frac{9}{2}}\right) - \left(1 - e^{-3}\right)$

$\qquad\qquad\quad = e^{-3} - e^{-\frac{9}{2}} = 0.039 \ (3 \text{ d.p.})$

14 $\int f(x)\,dx = 1 \Rightarrow \int_0^\infty ce^{-2x}\,dx$

$\qquad\qquad = c\left(-\frac{1}{2}e^{-2x}\right)_0^\infty$

$\qquad\qquad = \frac{c}{2} = 1 \Rightarrow c = 2$

As before, CDF, $F(x) = 1 - e^{-2x}$, $x > 0$

$\Rightarrow P(X > k) = 1 - P(X \le k = 1 - F(k)$

$\qquad\qquad\qquad = 1 - (1 - e^{-2k})$

$\qquad\qquad\qquad = e^{-2k}$

$P(X > t + k) = \ldots = e^{-2(t+k)}$

$P(X > t + k \mid X > k) = P\dfrac{(X > t + k \cap X > k)}{P(X > t)}$

$= \dfrac{P(X > t + t)}{P(X > k)}$

$= \dfrac{e^{-2(t+k)}}{e^{-2k}} = e^{-2t} = P(X > t)$ as required.

The waiting time until it fails is independent of the time it has already lasted.

The fact that they have been alight for 3 and 4 months is irrelevant.

We want $P\left(X > \frac{1}{4}\right) = e^{-\frac{1}{2}}$

$\Rightarrow$ for both, P(still alight in 3 months' time) $= \left(e^{-\frac{1}{2}}\right)^2$

$= e^{-1} = 0.368 \ (3 \text{ sig.figs.})$

15 Assuming calls are independent in t mins expect

$\frac{2t}{5}$ calls $\Rightarrow \lambda = \frac{2t}{5}$

(a) $P(\text{none}) = e^{-\lambda} = e^{-\frac{2t}{5}}$

(b) $P(\text{at least one}) = 1 - P(\text{none})$

$= 1 - e^{-\frac{2t}{5}}$

If X is waiting time, $P(X > t) = P(\text{no calls})$

$= e^{-\frac{2t}{5}}$

$\Rightarrow F(t) = P(X \le t) = 1 - P(X > t) = 1 - e^{-\frac{2t}{5}}$

$\Rightarrow f(t) = \dfrac{dF(t)}{dt} = \dfrac{2}{5}e^{-\frac{2t}{5}} = 0.4e^{-0.4t}$

(c) Mean time is $\frac{1}{\lambda} = \frac{5}{2}$ mins

(d) Median $\Rightarrow F(m) = \frac{1}{2} \Rightarrow 1 - e^{-\frac{2t}{5}} = \frac{1}{2}$

$e^{-\frac{2t}{5}} = 0.5$

$-0.4t = \ln 0.5$

$\Rightarrow t = \dfrac{\ln 0.5}{-0.4} = 1.73 \ (3 \text{ sig.figs.})$

(e) 3 mins irrelevant. P(none in 5 mins) $= e^{-2} = 0.135 \ (3 \text{ sig.figs.})$

Section 8

1 (i) $G(t) = \frac{1}{8} \times t^0 + \frac{1}{8} \times t^1$

$+ \frac{1}{4} \times t^2 + \frac{1}{3} \times t^3 + \frac{1}{6} \times t^4$

$= \frac{1}{8} + \frac{1}{8}t + \frac{1}{4}t^2 + \frac{1}{3}t^3 + \frac{1}{6}t^4$

(ii) $G(t) = \frac{1}{3}t^2 + \frac{1}{3}t^4 + \frac{1}{3}t^6$

2 Differentiating with respect to z,

$G'(z) = \dfrac{(2-z)\,1 - z(-1)}{(2-z)^2} = \dfrac{2}{(2-z)^2}$

$= 2(2-z)^{-2}$

Differentiating again,

$G''(z) = +4(2-z)^{-3}$

$\Rightarrow E(X) = G'(1) = 2$

$\text{Var}(X) = G''(1) + G'(1) - \left[G'(1)\right]^2$

$= 4 + 2 - 4 = 2$

3 Since $G(1) = 1$, $\dfrac{a}{b-2} = 1 \Rightarrow a = b - 2 \ldots\text{①}$

$G'(t) = 2a(b-2t)^{-2}$

$E(X) = G'(1) = \dfrac{2a}{(b-2)^2} = 4$

$\Rightarrow 2a = 4(b-2)^2 \Rightarrow a = 2(b-2)^2 \qquad \ldots\text{②}$

① and ② simultaneously, $b - 2 = 2(b-2)^2$

$\Rightarrow$ either $b = 2$ (not possible)

or $1 = 2(b-2) \Rightarrow b = \frac{5}{2}$

Into ①, $a = \frac{5}{2} - 2 = \frac{1}{2}$

4 (i) HH $\Rightarrow P(X = 2) = \frac{1}{4}$

(ii) THH $\Rightarrow P(X = 3) = \frac{1}{8}$

(iii) HTHH $\Rightarrow P(X = 4) = \frac{1}{8}$
TTHH

(iv) TTTHH $\Rightarrow P(X = 5) = \frac{3}{32}$
HTTHH
THTHH

(v) TTTTHH $\Rightarrow P(X = 6) = \frac{5}{64}$
TTHTHH
THTTHH
HTTTHH
HTHTHH

$G'(z) = \dfrac{(4 - 2z - z^2)(2z) - z^2(-2 - 2z)}{(4 - 2z - z^2)^2}$

$E(X) = G'(1) = \dfrac{2 - (-4)}{1} = 6$

5 The proof of the first part is in the text.
$G_x(t) = e^{\lambda(t-1)}$

Similarly, $G_y(t) = e^{\mu(t-1)}$

Since the PGF of $X + Y$ is given by

$G_{x+y}(t) = e^{\lambda(t-1)} e^{\mu(t-1)}$

$= e^{(\lambda + \mu)(t-1)}$

This is the PGF of a Poisson distribution with mean $\lambda + \mu$. When $\lambda = 1$ and $\mu = 2$, the mean is $1 + 2 = 3$.

$\Rightarrow P(X+Y = 4) = \dfrac{e^{-3}\,3^4}{4!} = 0.168$ (3 d.p's)

6 $P(N = n) = pq^{n-1}$

The next parts of the question, deriving the pgf for N and deducing that $E(N) = \dfrac{1}{p}$ and $\text{Var}(N) = \dfrac{q}{p^2}$ are covered in the text.

For the last part, M is the sum of two separate geometric distributions. The first variable, X say, is the number of throws before the event '5 or 6' occurs. This event has probability $\frac{2}{6} = \frac{1}{3}$ and so

$E(X) = \dfrac{1}{p} = \dfrac{1}{\frac{1}{3}} = 3$ and $\text{Var}(X) = \dfrac{q}{p^2}$

$= \dfrac{\frac{2}{3}}{\frac{1}{9}} = 6$

The second variable, Y say, is the number of throws before a 5 (or a 6, as appropriate) occurs to complete the pair. This event has probability $\frac{1}{6}$ and so

$E(Y) = \dfrac{1}{\frac{1}{6}} = 6$ and $\text{Var}(Y) = \dfrac{\frac{5}{6}}{\frac{1}{36}} = 30$

So $E(M) = E(X + Y) = t(x)\,t+(y)$

$= 6 + 3 = 9$

$\text{Var}(X + y) = \text{Var } X + \text{Var } Y$

$= 6 + 30 = 36$

(X and Y are independent)

7 (i) R has a geometric distribution with

$p = \frac{1}{6}$

$P(R = 1) = \frac{1}{6}$: $P(R = 2) = \frac{5}{6} \times \frac{1}{6}$

$P(R = 3) = \left(\frac{5}{6}\right)^2 \times \frac{1}{6}$

giving the pgf for R as

$G(z) = \frac{1}{6}z + \frac{5}{6} \times \frac{1}{6} \times z^2 + \left(\frac{5}{6}\right)^2 \times \frac{1}{6} \times z^3 + \cdots$

$= \frac{1}{6}z\left(\frac{1}{1 - \frac{5z}{6}}\right) = \frac{z}{6 - 5z}$

$= z(6 - 5z)^{-1}$

(ii) Since R has a geometric distribution,

$E(R) = \frac{1}{p} = \frac{1}{\frac{1}{6}} = 6$

and $\text{Var}(R) = \frac{q}{p^2} = \frac{\frac{5}{6}}{\frac{1}{36}} = 30$

(iii) In the binomial situation, with

$p = \frac{1}{6}, n = t - 1, r = 1$

$P(1 \text{ six in}(t - 1) \text{ throws})$

$= {}^nC_r \, p^r(1 - p)^{n - r}$

$= {}^{t-1}C_1\left(\frac{1}{6}\right)^1\left(\frac{5}{6}\right)^{t-2}$

But ${}^{t-1}C_1 = \frac{(t-1)!}{1!(t-2)!} = t - 1$

$\Rightarrow P(1 \text{ six}) = (t - 1) \times \left(\frac{1}{6}\right)^1\left(\frac{5}{6}\right)^{t-2}$

Probability of a six on the tth throw is $\frac{1}{6}$, so $P(2\text{nd six on } t\text{th throw})$

$= (t - 1)\left(\frac{1}{6}\right)^1\left(\frac{5}{6}\right)^{t-2} \times \frac{1}{6}$

$= (t - 1)\left(\frac{1}{6}\right)^2\left(\frac{5}{6}\right)^{t-2}$

$= (t - 1)\frac{1}{6^2} \times \frac{5^{t-2}}{6^{t-2}}$

$= (t - 1)\frac{5^{t-2}}{6^t}$

$= (t - 1)\,5^{t-2}\,6^{-t}$

8 (i) We can put the working in a table

Attempts before A wins	Outcomes necessary	Probability
1	A scores 1	a
2	A scores 0, B scores 0 then A scores 1	$(1 - a)(1 - b)$ (a)
3	A scores 0, B scores 0 then A scores 1	$(1 - a)^2$ $(1 - b)^2\,a$

So $P(A \text{ wins})$
$= a + (1 - a)(1 - b)\,a + (1 - a)^2(1 - b)^2\,a + \cdots$
$= \left[1 + \{(1 - a)(1 - b)\} + \{(1 - a)(1 - b)\}^2 + \cdots\right]a$

In the square brackets, we have an infinite geometric series, with first term 1 and common ratio $(1 - a)(1 - b)$

$[r < 1 \text{ since } 0 < a < 1, 0 < b < 1]$

This has a sum to infinity of

$\dfrac{1}{1 - \left[(1 - a)(1 - b)\right]}$

This gives $P(A \text{ wins})$

$= a \times \dfrac{1}{1 - (1 - a)(1 - b)}$

$= \dfrac{a}{a + b - ab}$

(ii) If $a = 0.1$ and $b = 0.2$, our table could be

Value of X	Outcomes	Probability
1	$A1$	$a = 0.1$
2	$A0B1$	$(1 - a)\,b = 0.9 \times 0.2$
3	$A0B0A1$	$(1 - a)(1 - b)a = 0.9 \times 0.8 \times 0.1$
4	$A0B0A0B1$	$(1 - a)^2(1 - b)\,b = 0.9^2 \times 0.8 \times 0.1$
5	$A0B0A0B0$ $A1$	$(1 - a)^2(1 - b)^2 a = 0.9^2 \times 0.8^2 \times 0.1$

We can see that if X is odd,

$P(X = n)$	$= 0.1$	$n = 1$
	$= 0.1 \times 0.9 \times 0.8$	$n = 3$
	$= 0.1 \times (0.9 \times 0.8)^2$	$n = 5$
	$= 0.1 \times (0.9 \times 0.8)^3$	$n = 7$

$$= 0.1 \times (0.9 \times 0.8)^{\frac{n-1}{2}} \text{ in general}$$

$$= 0.1 \, (0.72)^{\frac{n-1}{2}}$$

Similarly, if X is even,

$$
\begin{aligned}
P(X = n) &= 0.9 \times 0.2 & n &= 2 \\
&= 0.9 \times 0.2 \times [0.9 \times 0.8] & n &= 4 \\
&= 0.9 \times 0.2 \times [0.9 \times 0.8]^2 & n &= 6 \\
&= \dots
\end{aligned}
$$

$$= 0.9 \times 0.2 \times [0.9 \times 0.8]^{\frac{n-2}{2}}$$

in general

$$= 0.18 \, (0.72)^{\frac{n-2}{2}}$$

These two together give

$$
P(X = n)
\begin{cases}
\frac{1}{10} (0.72)^{\frac{n-1}{2}} & n \text{ odd} \\[2mm]
\frac{18}{100} (0.72)^{\frac{n-2}{2}} & n \text{ even}
\end{cases}
$$

(iii) The probability generation function of X, $G(t)$, is given by

$$G(t) = \frac{1}{10} t + \frac{18}{100} t^2 + \frac{1}{10} (0.72) \, t^3 + \frac{18}{100} (0.72) \, t^4 + \dots$$

$$= \left(\frac{1}{10} t + \frac{18}{100} \, t^2 \right) [1 + 0.72 t^2 + 0.72^2 t^4 + \dots]$$

The square bracket is an infinite GP, $a = 1$, $r = 0.72 t^2$

i.e. $G(t) = \left(\frac{1}{10} t + \frac{18}{100} \, t^2 \right) \left(\frac{1}{1 - 0.72 t^2} \right)$

Differentiating, $G'(t) =$

$$\frac{(1 - 0.72 t^2) \left(\frac{1}{10} + \frac{36}{100} t \right) - \left(\frac{1}{10} t + \frac{18}{100} \, t^2 \right) (-1.44 t)}{(1 - 0.72 t^2)^2}$$

$$\Rightarrow G'(1) = \frac{(0.28)(0.46) - (0.28)(-1.44)}{(0.28)^2}$$

$$= \frac{1.9}{0.28} = 6.8$$

Hence the mean number of games, $G'(1)$ is 7, to the nearest integer.

Section 9

1   (i) 4.76   (ii) 8.94

2   (i) 9.15   (ii) 6.51

3

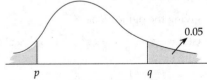

0.05

p q

From tables, $q = 6.16$

$$p = F_{6,4} (0.95) = \frac{1}{F_{4,6}(0.05)} = \frac{1}{4.53} = 0.22$$

i.e. $0.22 < X < 6.16$

4   (i)   We can code, using $Y = X - 85$. This gives the results as

Photometric	0.6	1.1	1.5	0.1	1.8	2.3	
Photographic	−2.6	−0.3	1.1	2.2	−2.6	0.8	−0.7

This gives $n_1 = 6, s_1^2 = 0.804^2$

$$n_2 = 7, s_2^2 = 1.833^2$$

The hypotheses are: $H_0: \sigma_1^2 = \sigma_2^2$

$$H_1: \sigma_1^2 \neq \sigma_2^2$$

two-tailed, 10% level $\Rightarrow F$ (5%), with $6 - 1$ $= 5$ and $7 - 1 = 6$ degrees of freedom.

$F_{5,6}$ (5%) $= 4.39$

Our test statistic is $F = \dfrac{s_2^2}{s_1^2} = \dfrac{1.833^2}{0.804^2} = 5.20$

Since this is less then the critical F-value, we accept the null hypothesis at the 5% level. The evidence suggests that there is no significant difference in variability between the two methods.

(ii)   The samples give

$$n_1 = 6 \quad \bar{x}_1 = 86.23 \quad s_1^2 = 0.804^2$$

$$n_2 = 7 \quad \bar{x}_2 = 84.70 \quad s_2^2 = 1.833^2$$

Our pooled estimate for the population variance is

$$s^2 = \frac{(6-1) \, 0.804^2 + (7-1) \, 1.833^2}{11}$$

$$= 2.13$$

No indication of direction, two-tailed test

$$H_0: \mu_1 = \mu_2$$

$$H_1: \mu_1 \neq \mu_2$$

At 5%, two-tailed, our critical value is
$t_{11}(2.5\%) = 2.20$

Our test statistic is

$$t = \frac{\bar{x}_1 - \bar{x}_2}{s\sqrt{\dfrac{1}{n_1} + \dfrac{1}{n_2}}} = \frac{86.23 - 84.7}{\sqrt{2.13\left(\frac{1}{6} + \frac{1}{7}\right)}}$$

$$= 1.88$$

This is not significant and we accept the null hypothesis. On the evidence, there is no significant difference in mean measurement between the methods.

5 The samples give $n_1 = 10$ $s_1^2 = 0.646^2$

$n_2 = 8$ $s_2^2 = 0.807^2$

There is an indication of direction, so one-tailed:

H_0: $\sigma_1^2 = \sigma_2^2$

H_1: $\sigma_1^2 < \sigma_2^2$

Since s_2^2 is the larger, we find $F_{7,9}\,(0.01)$

This is 5.64 (averaging).

Our test statistic is $F = \dfrac{s_2^2}{s_1^2} = \dfrac{0.807^2}{0.646^2} = 1.56$

This is not significant: on this evidence, there is no reason to doubt that the variances are the same.

The assumption is that the underlying distributions are normal.

The *t*-test requires that the underlying population variance be the same: from the test we have just carried out, this appears to be the case and we would be justified in carrying out a *t*-test.

6 We shall assume that the times are normally distributed and that the variance is the same for both groups. In this case, we can carry out a *t*-test for unpaired data.

(a) From the wording of the question, we can see that there is a definite indication of direction ('faster') and so we use a one-tailed test. Our null and alternative hypotheses are

H_0: $\mu_{\text{new}} = \mu_{\text{old}}$

H_1: $\mu_{\text{new}} < \mu_{\text{old}}$

(b) We calculate the values of $\bar{x}_1, \bar{x}_2, s_1$ and s_2 for the two samples.

New: $\bar{x}_1 = \dfrac{4.9 + 6.3 + \dots + 4.0}{7} = 5.9$ and
$s_1 = 1.995$ (calculator)

Old: $\bar{x}_2 = \dfrac{71.2}{9} = 7.911$

$s_2^2 = \dfrac{9}{8}\left(\dfrac{604.92}{9} - 7.911^2\right)$

$= 5.206$

We assume that the variance is the same for both samples, giving our unbiased estimate as

$$s^2 = \frac{(n_1 - 1)\,s_1^2 + (n_2 - 1)\,s_2^2}{n_1 + n_2 - 2}$$

$$= \frac{(7 - 1)\,1.995^2 + (9 - 1)\,5.206}{7 + 9 - 2}$$

$$= 4.68$$

Our *t*-value is given by

$$t = \frac{\bar{x}_1 - \bar{x}_2}{s\sqrt{\dfrac{1}{n_1} + \dfrac{1}{n_2}}} = \frac{5.9 - 7.91}{\sqrt{4.68}\,\sqrt{\dfrac{1}{7} + \dfrac{1}{9}}}$$

$$= -1.84$$

We have $16 - 2 = 14$ degrees of freedom
$t_{0.05,14} = \pm 1.761$

Our test value indicates a (just) significant result, and we reject the null hypothesis. On the basis of the given figures, there is evidence to support a decrease in time for the new language.

(c) A given pair of values would not be independent: the programmer would probably learn a strategy from the first attempt which would shorten a second attempt.

7 Since both the diameters are distributed normally we can use a paired *t*-test

H_0: $\mu_d = 0.6$ and H_1: $\mu_d > 0.6$

There are $(4 - 1) = 3$ degrees of freedom and $t_{0.005,3} = 2.35$

The differences are 0.72, 0.80, 0.90, 1.01

From the calculator, $\bar{d} = 0.8575$

$s_d = 0.1255$

This gives $t = \dfrac{\bar{d} - 0.6}{\dfrac{s_d}{\sqrt{n}}} = \dfrac{0.8575 - 0.6}{\dfrac{0.1255}{\sqrt{4}}}$

$$= 4.10$$

This is significantly greater than the critical value at the 5% level of 2.353, and we reject the null hypothesis. The observations indicate that the average difference is greater than 0.6 mm.

8 The conditions are that the populations have a normal distribution and equal variances, and that the samples are random and independent.

There is no indication of direction in the wording of the question, and we use a two-tailed test.

$$H_0: \mu_1 = \mu_2$$
$$H_1: \mu_1 \neq \mu_2$$

From tables, with $20 - 2 = 18$ degrees of freedom and a two-tailed test, $t_{0.025,\,18} = 2.101$

Using a calculator, $\mu_1 = 290.7$ $s_1 = 7.196$
$$\mu_2 = 284.7 \quad s_2 = 8.247$$

The variances appear to be more or less the same, confirming the suitability of a t-test. The pooled estimate of the common variance is

$$s^2 = \frac{s_1^2 + s_2^2}{2}$$

$$= \frac{7.196^2 + 8.247^2}{2}$$

$$= 59.90$$

Note that since the sample sizes are equal, the pooled estimate is just the average of the separate estimates.

The test statistics,

$$t = \frac{\overline{X}_1 - \overline{X}_2}{s \sqrt{\dfrac{1}{n_1} + \dfrac{1}{n_2}}}$$

$$= \frac{290.7 - 284.7}{\sqrt{59.90}\,\sqrt{\dfrac{1}{10} + \dfrac{1}{10}}} = 1.73$$

Since this is less than the critical value, the data do not provide evidence at the 5% significance level of a difference between mean reaction times.

A paired-sample t-test is more appropriate if the figures are in the correct order.

Again, a two-tailed test:

$$H_0: \overline{d} = 0$$

$$H_1: \overline{d} \neq 0$$

$10 - 1 = 9$ degrees of freedom, $t_9 (2.5\%) = 2.262$

Differences are 8, –5, 13, –3, 9, –2, 10, 4, 11, 15

From calculator, $\overline{d} = 6$ $s_d = 7.10$

$$t = \frac{\overline{d}}{\dfrac{s_d}{\sqrt{n}}} = \frac{6}{\dfrac{7.10}{\sqrt{10}}} = 2.67$$

This is greater than the critical value, so we reject H_0. The evidence suggests a difference in mean times at the 5% level.

9 Since the data are paired, the appropriate t-test is the paired t-test. This can be used if we assume that the differences have a normal distribution.

Computing the differences and calling their mean μ_d,

$$H_0: \mu_d = 0$$
$$H_1: \mu_d \neq 0$$

It is a two-tailed test with $8 - 1 = 7$ degrees of freedom. If we carry out the test to a 1% level of significance, our critical value for t is

$$t_7 (1\%) = 2.998$$

The differences are

2   –4   8   6   14   0   –4   –3

This gives $\overline{X}_d = 2.375$ $s_d = 6.5$

Our test statistic is $t = \dfrac{2.375}{\dfrac{6.5}{\sqrt{8}}} = 1.03$

This is not significant and there is no reason to reject the null hypothesis on this evidence, i.e. the papers appear to be of equivalent level of difficulty.

Section 10

1 (a) The coding used does not affect the working, since $\text{Var}(X + a) = \text{Var}(X)$ when a is constant.

We use the ANOVA method; since the totals and numbers are given, we can proceed immediately to a calculation of the sums of squares:

Total $SS_T = \Sigma x_{ij}^2 - \dfrac{G^2}{n} = 39129 - \dfrac{1218^2}{63}$

$= 14581$

Between $SS_B = (T_1^2, n_1) + \dfrac{T_2^2}{n_2} + \dfrac{T_3^2}{n_3} - \dfrac{G^2}{N}$

$= \dfrac{508^2}{24} + \dfrac{546^2}{22} + \dfrac{164^2}{17} - \dfrac{1218^2}{63}$

$= 2337.5$

Within $SS_W = SS_T - SS_B$

$= 14581 - 2337.5$

$= 12243.5$

Our ANOVA table becomes

Source	SS	df	MS	F-ratio
Between	2337.5	3 − 1 = 2	1169	5.73
Within	12243.5	63 − 3 = 60	204	
Total	14581	62		

Our null hypothesis is that the means are equal, and the alternative is that they are not.

H_0: $\mu_A = \mu_B = \mu_C$

H_1: Differences between the means.

Looking up $F_{0.05}$, 2, 60 we find the critical value given at 3.15

Our F-ratio is significantly larger than this and we reject the null hypothesis. The evidence suggests that the means are significantly different (we would probably expect this result if we look at the mean of class C compared with the other two).

(b) We have assumed that the marks are distributed normally.

(c) She should use an unpaired t-text: this makes the same assumption as (b)

2 Our table is

Design	1	2	3	4	
A	17	4	38	8	$67 = R_1$
B	21	6	52	20	$99 = R_2$
C	28	9	64	22	$123 = R_3$
	$66 = T_1$	$19 = T_2$	$154 = T_3$	$50 = T_4$	$289 = G$

As always, we check that the rows and columns have the same total.

We are given that $SS_T = 3878.9$ so we can proceed to the other sums of squares.

Employees: $SS_E = \dfrac{66^2 + 19^2 + 154^2 + 50^2}{3}$

$- \dfrac{289^2}{12} = 10311 - 6960.1 = 3350.9$

Design $SS_D = \dfrac{67^2 + 99^2 + 123^2}{4} - \dfrac{289^2}{12}$

$= 7354.8 - 6960.1 = 394.7$

Residual $SS_R = SS_T - SS_E - SS_D$

$= 3878.9 - 3350.9 - 394.7$

$= 133.3$

Our ANOVA table becomes

Source	SS	df	MS	F-ratio
Employees	3350.9	3	1117	50.3
Design	394.7	2	197.4	8.89
Residual	133.3	6	22.2	
Total	3878.9	11		

Designs: H_0: $\mu_A = \mu_B = \mu_C$

H_1: μ_A, μ_B and μ_C are not all equal.

At 5% level, $F_{0.05}$, 2, 6 = 5.14

Our test result is significant: the evidence suggests that there is a difference between the assembly times for the various designs

Employees: H_0: $\mu_1 = \mu_2 = \mu_3 = \mu_4$

H_1: μ_1, μ_2, μ_3 and μ_4

At 5% level, $F_{0.05}$, 3, 6 = 4.76

Our test result is highly significant: the evidence pointed to a large difference in assembly times between employees.

3 We calculate

	A	B	C	
1	12	15	6	$R_1 = 33$
2	60	45	30	$R_2 = 135$
	$C_1 = 72$	$C_2 = 60$	$C_3 = 36$	$G = 168$

$$SS_{Firm} = \frac{33^2 + 135^2}{3} - \frac{168^2}{6} = 1734$$

$$SS_{Type} = \frac{72^2 + 60^2 + 36^2}{2} - \frac{168^2}{6} = 336$$

(as a check)

$$SS_{Residual} = 2226 - 1734 - 336 = 156$$

We can now fill in our table

Source	Degrees of freedom	Sum of squares	Mean square	Ratio
Firm	1	1734	1734	22.23
Type	2	336	168	2.15
Residual	2	156	78	
Total	5	2226		

H_0: no difference in mean cost between firms

H_1: difference in mean cost between firms

At 5%, df 1 and 2 respectively, $F_{1,2}$ (5%) = 18.51

The F-ratio exceeds this and so we reject the null hypothesis. The given data provide significant evidence for mean difference in cost between firms.

4 (a) Assuming a normal distribution and equal variance within methods, we can sum for the different diets.

Diet	A	B	C	
	31	12	31	
	23	54	70	
	38	29	25	
	54		51	
			44	
	146	95	221	462
	$= T_A$	$= T_B$	$= T_C$	$= G$

Between diets: $SS_B = \dfrac{T_A^2}{n_A} + \dfrac{T_B^2}{n_B} + \dfrac{T_C^2}{n_C} - \dfrac{G^2}{n}$

$$= \frac{146^2}{4} + \frac{95^2}{3} + \frac{221^2}{5} - \frac{462^2}{12}$$

$$= 318.5$$

Total: $SS_T = $ (Sum of squares) $- \dfrac{G^2}{n}$

$$= 20774 - \frac{462^2}{12}$$

$$= 2987$$

Within diets: $SS_W = SS_T - SS_B$

$$= 2987 - 318.53 = 2668.5$$

Degrees of freedom:

Between df	$= 3 - 1 = 2$
Total	$= 12 - 1 = 11$
Within	$= 11 - 2 = 9$

Our ANOVA table is

Source	SS	df	MS	F-ratio
Between	318.5	2	159.3	0.537
Within	2668.5	9	296.5	
Total	2987	11		

This is certainly not significant (the within sum of squares is so large). At 5%, $F_{2,9} = 4.26$

(b) Our ANOVA for two-way analysis is

Source	SS	df	MS
Between diets	337	2	168.5
Between initial weights	649	2	324.5
Error	86	4	21.5
Total	1072	8	

Our test statistic for the diets is

$$F = \frac{168.5}{21.5} = 7.84$$

At the 5% level, $F_{2,4} = 6.94$, i.e. significant.

For the initial weights, $F = \dfrac{324.5}{21.5} = 15.09$ i.e. significant.

The evidence suggests a significant difference between diets and between initial weights.

(c) The very large within sum of squares in the previous analysis has been reduced by more careful planning of the experiment, taking account of factors thought liable to affect the response variable. It is also better to have a balanced experiment when using small numbers (i.e. the same number allotted to each diet).

The evidence points to a significant difference in weight loss *in males* between diets (and confirms the suspicion that initial weight is a significant factor). To widen the conclusion to include females we would have to carry out a further experiment.

5 (a) $\dfrac{34.1 + 30.1}{2} = 32.1$

(b) Our table becomes

	A	B	C	D	E	
1	31.0	33.5	28.0	40.1	34.1	$166.7 = S_1$
2	29.5	31.4	25.0	30.2	32.1	$148.2 = S_2$
3	22.7	32.1	26.4	29.8	30.1	$141.1 = S_3$
	83.2	97.0	79.4	100.1	96.3	456.0
	$= T_A$	$= T_B$	$= T_C$	$= T_D$	$= T_E$	$= G$

Between cars: $\dfrac{T_A^2 + \ldots + T_E^2}{3} - \dfrac{G^2}{n}$

$= 13976.4 - \dfrac{456^2}{15}$

$= 114.0$

Between petrols: $\dfrac{S_1^2 + S_2^2 + S_3^2}{5} - \dfrac{G^2}{n}$

$= 13932.3 - \dfrac{456^2}{15}$

$= 69.9$

Total: Squares $- \dfrac{G^2}{n} = 14098.4 - \dfrac{456^2}{15}$

$= 236.0$

Residual:

Total – Between cars – Between petrols

$= 236.0 - 114.0 - 69.9$

$= 52.1$

df: Cars $5 - 1 = 4$
      Petrols $3 - 1 = 2$
      Total $15 - 1 = 14$
      Residual $14 - 2 - 4 = 8$

Our ANOVA table is

Source	SS	df	MS
Between cars	114.0	4	28.5
Between petrols	69.9	2	35.0
Residual	52.1	8	6.5
Total	236.0	14	

Between cars: F-ratio is $\dfrac{28.5}{6.5} = 4.38$

$F_{4,8}$ at 5% is 3.84, i.e. significant.

Between petrols: F-ratio is $\dfrac{35.0}{6.5} = 5.38$

$F_{2,8}$ at 5% is 4.46, i.e. significant

The evidence suggests significant differences between makes of car and between brands of petrol.

Appendix 1: Random numbers

86 13	84 10	07 30	39 05	97 96	88 07	37 26	04 89	13 48	19 20
60 78	48 12	99 47	09 46	91 33	17 21	03 94	79 00	08 50	40 16
78 48	03 37	82 26	01 06	64 65	94 41	17 26	74 66	61 93	24 97
80 56	90 79	66 94	18 40	97 79	93 20	41 51	25 04	20 71	76 04
99 09	39 25	66 31	70 56	30 15	52 17	87 55	31 11	10 68	98 23
56 32	32 72	91 65	97 36	56 61	12 79	95 17	57 16	53 58	96 36
66 02	49 93	97 44	99 15	56 86	80 57	11 78	40 23	58 40	86 14
31 77	53 94	05 93	56 14	71 23	60 46	05 33	23 72	93 10	81 23
98 79	72 43	14 76	54 77	66 29	84 09	88 56	75 86	41 67	04 42
50 97	92 15	10 01	57 01	87 33	73 17	70 18	40 21	24 20	66 62
90 51	94 50	12 48	88 95	09 34	09 30	22 27	25 56	40 76	01 59
31 99	52 24	13 43	27 88	11 39	41 65	00 84	13 06	31 79	74 97
22 96	23 34	46 12	67 11	48 06	99 24	14 83	78 37	65 73	39 47
06 84	55 41	27 06	74 59	14 29	20 14	45 75	31 16	05 41	22 96
08 64	89 30	25 25	71 35	33 31	04 56	12 67	03 74	07 16	49 32
86 87	62 43	15 11	76 49	79 13	78 80	93 89	09 57	07 14	40 74
94 44	97 13	77 04	35 02	12 76	60 91	93 40	81 06	85 85	72 84
63 25	55 14	66 47	99 90	02 90	83 43	16 01	19 69	11 78	87 16
11 22	83 98	15 21	18 57	53 42	91 91	26 52	89 13	86 00	47 61
01 70	10 83	94 71	13 67	11 12	36 54	53 32	90 43	79 01	95 15

Appendix 2: The normal distribution function

The function tabulated below is $\Phi(z)$, defined as $\Phi(z) = \dfrac{1}{\sqrt{2\pi}} \displaystyle\int_{-\infty}^{z} e^{-\frac{1}{2}t^2}\, dt.$

z	$\Phi(z)$	z	$\Phi(z)$	z	$\Phi(z)$	z	$\Phi(z)$	z	$\Phi(z)$
0.00	0.5000	0.50	0.6915	1.00	0.8413	1.50	0.9332	2.00	0.9772
0.01	0.5040	0.51	0.6950	1.01	0.8438	1.51	0.9345	2.02	0.9783
0.02	0.5080	0.52	0.6985	1.02	0.8461	1.52	0.9357	2.04	0.9793
0.03	0.5120	0.53	0.7019	1.03	0.8485	1.53	0.9370	2.06	0.9803
0.04	0.5160	0.54	0.7054	1.04	0.8508	1.54	0.9382	2.08	0.9812
0.05	0.5199	0.55	0.7088	1.05	0.8531	1.55	0.9394	2.10	0.9821
0.06	0.5239	0.56	0.7123	1.06	0.8554	1.56	0.9406	2.12	0.9830
0.07	0.5279	0.57	0.7157	1.07	0.8577	1.57	0.9418	2.14	0.9838
0.08	0.5319	0.58	0.7190	1.08	0.8599	1.58	0.9429	2.16	0.9846
0.09	0.5359	0.59	0.7224	1.09	0.8621	1.59	0.9441	2.18	0.9854
0.10	0.5398	0.60	0.7257	1.10	0.8643	1.60	0.9452	2.20	0.9861
0.11	0.5438	0.61	0.7291	1.11	0.8665	1.61	0.9463	2.22	0.9868
0.12	0.5478	0.62	0.7324	1.12	0.8686	1.62	0.9474	2.24	0.9875
0.13	0.5517	0.63	0.7357	1.13	0.8708	1.63	0.9484	2.26	0.9881
0.14	0.5557	0.64	0.7389	1.14	0.8729	1.64	0.9495	2.28	0.9887
0.15	0.5596	0.65	0.7422	1.15	0.8749	1.65	0.9505	2.30	0.9893
0.16	0.5636	0.66	0.7454	1.16	0.8770	1.66	0.9515	2.32	0.9898
0.17	0.5675	0.67	0.7486	1.17	0.8790	1.67	0.9525	2.34	0.9904
0.18	0.5714	0.68	0.7517	1.18	0.8810	1.68	0.9535	2.36	0.9909
0.19	0.5753	0.69	0.7549	1.19	0.8830	1.69	0.9545	2.38	0.9913
0.20	0.5793	0.70	0.7580	1.20	0.8849	1.70	0.9554	2.40	0.9918
0.21	0.5832	0.71	0.7611	1.21	0.8869	1.71	0.9564	2.42	0.9922
0.22	0.5871	0.72	0.7642	1.22	0.8888	1.72	0.9573	2.44	0.9927
0.23	0.5910	0.73	0.7673	1.23	0.8907	1.73	0.9582	2.46	0.9931
0.24	0.5948	0.74	0.7704	1.24	0.8925	1.74	0.9591	2.48	0.9934
0.25	0.5987	0.75	0.7734	1.25	0.8944	1.75	0.9599	2.50	0.9938
0.26	0.6026	0.76	0.7764	1.26	0.8962	1.76	0.9608	2.55	0.9946
0.27	0.6064	0.77	0.7794	1.27	0.8980	1.77	0.9616	2.60	0.9953
0.28	0.6103	0.78	0.7823	1.28	0.8997	1.78	0.9625	2.65	0.9960
0.29	0.6141	0.79	0.7852	1.29	0.9015	1.79	0.9633	2.70	0.9965
0.30	0.6179	0.80	0.7881	1.30	0.9032	1.80	0.9641	2.75	0.9970
0.31	0.6217	0.81	0.7910	1.31	0.9049	1.81	0.9649	2.80	0.9974
0.32	0.6255	0.82	0.7939	1.32	0.9066	1.82	0.9656	2.85	0.9978
0.33	0.6293	0.83	0.7967	1.33	0.9082	1.83	0.9664	2.90	0.9981
0.34	0.6331	0.84	0.7995	1.34	0.9099	1.84	0.9671	2.95	0.9984
0.35	0.6368	0.85	0.8023	1.35	0.9115	1.85	0.9678	3.00	0.9987
0.36	0.6406	0.86	0.8051	1.36	0.9131	1.86	0.9686	3.05	0.9989
0.37	0.6443	0.87	0.8078	1.37	0.9147	1.87	0.9693	3.10	0.9990
0.38	0.6480	0.88	0.8106	1.38	0.9162	1.88	0.9699	3.15	0.9992
0.39	0.6517	0.89	0.8133	1.39	0.9177	1.89	0.9706	3.20	0.9993
0.40	0.6554	0.90	0.8159	1.40	0.9192	1.90	0.9713	3.25	0.9994
0.41	0.6591	0.91	0.8186	1.41	0.9207	1.91	0.9719	3.30	0.9995
0.42	0.6628	0.92	0.8212	1.42	0.9222	1.92	0.9726	3.35	0.9996
0.43	0.6664	0.93	0.8238	1.43	0.9236	1.93	0.9732	3.40	0.9997
0.44	0.6700	0.94	0.8264	1.44	0.9251	1.94	0.9738	3.50	0.9998
0.45	0.6736	0.95	0.8289	1.45	0.9265	1.95	0.9744	3.60	0.9998
0.46	0.6772	0.96	0.8315	1.46	0.9279	1.96	0.9750	3.70	0.9999
0.47	0.6808	0.97	0.8340	1.47	0.9292	1.97	0.9756	3.80	0.9999
0.48	0.6844	0.98	0.8365	1.48	0.9306	1.98	0.9761	3.90	1.0000
0.49	0.6879	0.99	0.8389	1.49	0.9319	1.99	0.9767	4.00	1.0000
0.50	0.6915	1.00	0.8413	1.50	0.9332	2.00	0.9772		

Percentage points of the normal distribution

The values z in the table are those which a random variable $Z \sim N(0,1)$ exceeds with probability p; that is, $P(Z > z) = 1 - \Phi(z) = p$.

p	z	p	z
0.5000	0.0000	0.05000	1.6449
0.4000	0.2533	0.0250	1.9600
0.3000	0.5244	0.0100	3.3263
0.2000	0.8416	0.0050	2.5758
0.1500	1.0364	0.0010	3.0902
0.1000	1.2816	0.0005	3.2905

Appendix 3: Percentage points of the χ^2-distribution

The values in the table are those which a random variable with the χ^2 distribution on v degrees of freedom exceeds with the probability shown.

v	0.995	0.990	0.975	0.950	0.900	0.100	0.050	0.025	0.010	0.005
1	0.000	0.000	0.001	0.004	0.016	2.705	3.841	5.024	6.635	7.879
2	0.010	0.020	0.051	0.103	0.211	4.605	5.991	7.378	9.210	10.597
3	0.072	0.115	0.216	0.352	0.584	6.251	7.815	9.348	11.345	12.838
4	0.207	0.297	0.484	0.711	1.064	7.779	9.488	11.143	13.277	14.860
5	0.412	0.554	0.831	1.145	1.610	9.236	11.070	12.832	15.086	16.750
6	0.676	0.872	1.237	1.635	2.204	10.645	12.592	14.449	16.812	18.548
7	0.989	1.239	1.690	2.167	2.833	12.017	14.067	16.013	18.475	20.278
8	1.344	1.646	2.180	2.733	3.490	13.362	15.507	17.535	20.090	21.955
9	1.735	2.088	2.700	3.325	4.168	14.684	16.919	19.023	21.666	23.589
10	2.156	2.558	3.247	3.940	4.865	15.987	18.307	20.483	23.209	25.188
11	2.603	3.053	3.816	4.575	5.580	17.275	19.675	21.920	24.725	26.757
12	3.074	3.571	4.404	5.226	6.304	18.549	21.026	23.337	26.217	28.300
13	3.565	4.107	5.009	5.892	7.042	19.812	22.362	24.736	27.688	29.819
14	4.075	4.660	5.629	6.571	7.790	21.064	23.685	26.119	29.141	31.319
15	4.601	5.229	6.262	7.261	8.547	22.307	24.996	27.488	30.578	32.801
16	5.142	5.812	6.908	7.962	9.312	23.542	26.296	28.845	32.000	34.267
17	5.697	6.408	7.564	8.672	10.085	24.769	27.587	30.191	33.409	35.718
18	6.265	7.015	8.231	9.390	10.865	25.989	28.869	31.526	34.805	37.156
19	6.844	7.633	8.907	10.117	11.651	27.204	30.144	32.852	36.191	38.582
20	7.434	8.260	9.591	10.851	12.443	28.412	31.410	34.170	37.566	39.997
21	8.034	8.897	10.283	11.591	13.240	29.615	32.671	35.479	38.932	41.401
22	8.643	9.542	10.982	12.338	14.042	30.813	33.924	36.781	40.289	42.796
23	9.260	10.196	11.689	13.091	14.848	32.007	35.172	38.076	41.638	44.181
24	9.886	10.856	12.401	13.848	15.659	33.196	36.415	39.364	42.980	45.558
25	10.520	11.524	13.120	14.611	16.473	34.382	37.652	40.646	44.314	46.928
26	11.160	12.198	13.844	15.379	17.292	35.563	38.885	41.923	45.642	48.290
27	11.808	12.879	14.573	16.151	18.114	36.741	40.113	43.194	46.963	49.645
28	12.461	13.565	15.308	16.928	18.939	37.916	41.337	44.461	48.278	50.993
29	13.121	14.256	16.047	17.708	19.768	39.088	42.557	45.722	49.588	52.336
30	13.787	14.953	16.791	18.493	20.599	40.256	43.773	46.979	50.892	53.672

Appendix 4: Poisson cumulative distribution function

The tabulated value is $P(X \leq x)$, where X has a Poisson distribution with parameter μ.

$\mu =$	0.5	1.0	1.5	2.0	2.5	3.0	3.5	4.0	4.5	5.0
$x = 0$	0.6065	0.3679	0.2231	0.1353	0.0821	0.0498	0.0302	0.0183	0.0111	0.0067
1	0.9098	0.7358	0.5578	0.4060	0.2873	0.1991	0.1359	0.0916	0.0611	0.0404
2	0.9856	0.9197	0.8088	0.6767	0.5438	0.4232	0.3208	0.2381	0.1736	0.1247
3	0.9982	0.9810	0.9344	0.8571	0.7576	0.6472	0.5366	0.4335	0.3423	0.2650
4	0.9998	0.9963	0.9814	0.9473	0.8912	0.8153	0.7254	0.6288	0.5321	0.4405
5	1.0000	0.9994	0.9955	0.9834	0.9580	0.9161	0.8576	0.7851	0.7029	0.6160
6	1.0000	0.9999	0.9991	0.9955	0.9858	0.9665	0.9347	0.8893	0.8311	0.7622
7	1.0000	1.0000	0.9998	0.9989	0.9958	0.9881	0.9733	0.9489	0.9134	0.8666
8	1.0000	1.0000	1.0000	0.9998	0.9989	0.9962	0.9901	0.9786	0.9597	0.9319
9	1.0000	1.0000	1.0000	1.0000	0.9997	0.9989	0.9967	0.9919	0.9829	0.9682
10	1.0000	1.0000	1.0000	1.0000	0.9999	0.9997	0.9990	0.9972	0.9933	0.9863
11	1.0000	1.0000	1.0000	1.0000	1.0000	0.9999	0.9997	0.9991	0.9976	0.9945
12	1.0000	1.0000	1.0000	1.0000	1.0000	1.0000	0.9999	0.9997	0.9992	0.9980
13	1.0000	1.0000	1.0000	1.0000	1.0000	1.0000	1.0000	0.9999	0.9997	0.9993
14	1.0000	1.0000	1.0000	1.0000	1.0000	1.0000	1.0000	1.0000	0.9999	0.9998
15	1.0000	1.0000	1.0000	1.0000	1.0000	1.0000	1.0000	1.0000	1.0000	0.9999
16	1.0000	1.0000	1.0000	1.0000	1.0000	1.0000	1.0000	1.0000	1.0000	1.0000
17	1.0000	1.0000	1.0000	1.0000	1.0000	1.0000	1.0000	1.0000	1.0000	1.0000
18	1.0000	1.0000	1.0000	1.0000	1.0000	1.0000	1.0000	1.0000	1.0000	1.0000
19	1.0000	1.0000	1.0000	1.0000	1.0000	1.0000	1.0000	1.0000	1.0000	1.0000

$\mu =$	5.5	6.0	6.5	7.0	7.5	8.0	8.5	9.0	9.5	10.0
$x = 0$	0.0041	0.0025	0.0015	0.0009	0.0006	0.0003	0.0002	0.0001	0.0001	0.0000
1	0.0266	0.0174	0.0113	0.0073	0.0047	0.0030	0.0019	0.0012	0.0008	0.0005
2	0.0884	0.0620	0.0430	0.0296	0.0203	0.0138	0.0093	0.0062	0.0042	0.0028
3	0.2017	0.1512	0.1118	0.0818	0.0591	0.0424	0.0301	0.0212	0.0149	0.0103
4	0.3575	0.2851	0.2237	0.1730	0.1321	0.0996	0.0744	0.0550	0.0403	0.0293
5	0.5289	0.4457	0.3690	0.3007	0.2414	0.1912	0.1496	0.1157	0.0885	0.0671
6	0.6860	0.6063	0.5265	0.4497	0.3782	0.3134	0.2562	0.2068	0.1649	0.1301
7	0.8095	0.7440	0.6728	0.5987	0.5246	0.4530	0.3856	0.3239	0.2687	0.2202
8	0.8944	0.8472	0.7916	0.7291	0.6620	0.5925	0.5231	0.4557	0.3918	0.3328
9	0.9462	0.9161	0.8774	0.8305	0.7764	0.7166	0.6530	0.5874	0.5218	0.4579
10	0.9747	0.9574	0.9332	0.9015	0.8622	0.8159	0.7634	0.7060	0.6453	0.5830
11	0.9890	0.9799	0.9661	0.9467	0.9208	0.8881	0.8487	0.8030	0.7520	0.6968
12	0.9955	0.9912	0.9840	0.9730	0.9573	0.9362	0.9091	0.8758	0.8364	0.7916
13	0.9983	0.9964	0.9929	0.9872	0.9784	0.9658	0.9486	0.9261	0.8981	0.8645
14	0.9994	0.9986	0.9970	0.9943	0.9897	0.9827	0.9726	0.9585	0.9400	0.9165
15	0.9998	0.9995	0.9988	0.9976	0.9954	0.9918	0.9862	0.9780	0.9665	0.9513
16	0.9999	0.9998	0.9996	0.9990	0.9980	0.9963	0.9934	0.9889	0.9823	0.9730
17	1.0000	0.9999	0.9998	0.9996	0.9992	0.9984	0.9970	0.9947	0.9911	0.9857
18	1.0000	1.0000	0.9999	0.9999	0.9997	0.9993	0.9987	0.9976	0.9957	0.9928
19	1.0000	1.0000	1.0000	1.0000	0.9999	0.9997	0.9995	0.9989	0.9980	0.9965
20	1.0000	1.0000	1.0000	1.0000	1.0000	0.9999	0.9998	0.9996	0.9991	0.9984
21	1.0000	1.0000	1.0000	1.0000	1.0000	1.0000	0.9999	0.9998	0.9996	0.9993
22	1.0000	1.0000	1.0000	1.0000	1.0000	1.0000	1.0000	0.9999	0.9999	0.9997

Appendix 5: Wilcoxon rank-sum test

The table below gives the largest value for the rank-sum statistic T leading to statistical significance at the level shown, on a one-tailed test. The sample whose ranks are summed is of size n_1, and the second sample is of size n_2.

0.025 level

n_2/n_1	5	6	7	8	9	10	11	12	13	14	15	16	17	18	19	20
5	17															
6	18	26														
7	20	27	36													
8	21	29	38	49												
9	22	31	40	51	62											
10	23	32	42	53	65	78										
11	24	34	44	55	68	81	96									
12	26	35	46	58	71	84	99	115								
13	27	37	48	60	73	88	103	119	136							
14	28	38	50	62	76	91	106	123	141	160						
15	29	40	52	65	79	94	110	127	145	164	184					
16	30	42	54	67	82	97	113	131	150	169	190	211				
17	32	43	56	70	84	100	117	135	154	174	195	217	240			
18	33	45	58	72	87	103	121	139	158	179	200	222	246	270		
19	34	46	60	74	90	107	124	143	163	183	205	228	252	277	303	
20	35	48	62	77	93	110	128	147	167	188	210	234	258	283	309	337

0.05 level

n_2/n_1	5	6	7	8	9	10	11	12	13	14	15	16	17	18	19	20
5	19															
6	20	28														
7	21	29	39													
8	23	31	41	51												
9	24	33	43	54	66											
10	26	35	45	56	69	82										
11	27	37	47	59	72	86	100									
12	28	38	49	62	75	89	104	120								
13	30	40	52	64	78	92	108	125	142							
14	31	42	54	67	81	96	112	129	147	166						
15	33	44	56	69	84	99	116	133	152	171	192					
16	34	46	58	72	87	103	120	138	156	176	197	219				
17	35	47	61	75	90	106	123	142	161	182	203	225	249			
18	37	49	63	77	93	110	127	146	166	187	208	231	255	280		
19	38	51	65	80	96	113	131	150	171	192	214	237	262	287	313	
20	40	53	67	83	99	117	135	155	175	197	220	243	268	294	320	348

Wilcoxon signed rank-sum test

The table below gives the largest value for the signed rank statistic S leading to statistical significance at the level shown, on a one-tailed test.

	Significance level			
	0.05	0.025	0.01	0.005
5	0			
6	2	0		
7	3	2	0	
8	5	3	1	0
9	8	5	3	1
10	10	8	5	3
11	13	10	7	5
12	17	13	9	7
13	21	17	12	9
14	25	21	15	12
15	30	25	19	15
16	35	29	23	19
17	41	34	27	23
18	47	40	32	27
19	53	46	37	32
20	60	52	43	37

Appendix 6: Percentage points of student's *t* distribution

The values in the table are those which a random variable with student's *t* distribution on v degrees of freedom exceeds with the probability shown.

v	0.10	0.05	0.025	0.01	0.005
1	3.078	6.314	12.706	31.821	63.657
2	1.886	2.920	4.303	6.965	9.925
3	1.638	2.353	3.182	4.541	5.841
4	1.533	2.132	2.776	3.747	4.604
5	1.476	2.015	2.571	3.365	4.032
6	1.440	1.943	2.447	3.143	3.707
7	1.415	1.895	2.365	2.998	3.499
8	1.397	1.860	2.306	2.896	3.355
9	1.383	1.833	2.262	2.821	3.250
10	1.372	1.812	2.228	2.764	3.169
11	1.363	1.796	2.201	2.718	3.106
12	1.356	1.782	2.179	2.681	3.055
13	1.350	1.771	2.160	2.650	3.012
14	1.345	1.761	2.145	2.624	2.977
15	1.341	1.753	2.131	2.602	2.947
16	1.337	1.746	2.120	2.583	2.921
17	1.333	1.740	2.110	2.567	2.898
18	1.330	1.734	2.101	2.552	2.878
19	1.328	1.729	2.093	2.539	2.861
20	1.325	1.725	2.086	2.528	2.845
21	1.323	1.721	2.080	2.518	2.831
22	1.321	1.717	2.074	2.508	2.819
23	1.319	1.714	2.069	2.500	2.807
24	1.318	1.711	2.064	2.492	2.797
25	1.316	1.708	2.060	2.485	2.787
26	1.315	1.706	2.056	2.479	2.779
27	1.314	1.703	2.052	2.473	2.771
28	1.313	1.701	2.048	2.467	2.763
29	1.311	1.699	2.045	2.462	2.756
30	1.310	1.697	2.042	2.457	2.750
32	1.309	1.694	2.037	2.449	2.738
34	1.307	1.691	2.032	2.441	2.728
36	1.306	1.688	2.028	2.435	2.719
38	1.304	1.686	2.024	2.429	2.712
40	1.303	1.684	2.021	2.423	2.704

Contd.

Percentage points of the student's t-distribution contd.

v	0.10	0.05	0.025	0.01	0.005
45	1.301	1.679	2.014	2.412	2.690
50	1.299	1.676	2.009	2.403	2.678
55	1.297	1.673	2.004	2.396	2.668
60	1.296	1.671	2.000	2.390	2.660
70	1.294	1.667	1.994	2.381	2.648
80	1.292	1.664	1.990	2.374	2.639
90	1.291	1.662	1.987	2.369	2.632
100	1.290	1.660	1.984	2.364	2.626
110	1.289	1.659	1.982	2.361	2.621
120	1.289	1.658	1.980	2.358	2.617